Independent Schools
Examinations Board

MATHS PRACTICE EXERCISES 13+ LEVEL 3

David E Hanson

Independent Schools
Examinations Board

www.galorepark.co.uk

GALORE PARK

Published by ISEB Publications, an imprint of Galore Park Publishing Ltd

19/21 Sayers Lane, Tenterden, Kent TN30 6BW
www.galorepark.co.uk

Text copyright © David E Hanson 2012

The right of David E Hanson to be identified as the author of this work has
been asserted by him in accordance with sections 77 and 78 of the Copyright,
Designs and Patents Act 1988.

Design and typesetting Typetechnique
Printed and bound by Charlesworth Press, Wakefield

ISBN 978 1 907047 75 6

First published 2012, reprinted 2012, 2013

Details of other ISEB Revision Guides for Common Entrance, examination
papers and Galore Park publications are available at www.galorepark.co.uk

Front cover photograph: Light beams through glass prism
© Corbis Cusp/Alamy

About the author

David Hanson has over 40 years' experience of teaching and has been Leader of the ISEB 11+ Maths setting team and a member of the ISEB Editorial Board. He has also edited the SATIPS Maths Broadsheet. David recently retired from teaching to run a small shop trading in collectors' items.

Acknowledgements

I would like to thank Gina de Cova once again for her generous assistance at various stages of this latest publication.

David Hanson
July 2012

Contents

Numbers

Questions involving

- multiples and factors
- prime numbers
- negative numbers
- place value
- ordering
- estimation and approximation

Questions involving

- fractions
- decimals
- percentages
- ratio and proportion

Calculations

Mixed questions

Mixed questions

Mixed questions

Solving problems

Mixed questions

Mixed questions

Algebra

Questions involving

- terms and expressions
- simplification; brackets
- substitution
- equations
- inequalities
- formulae
- modelling
- trial and improvement

Questions involving

- sequences
- linear functions and their graphs
- quadratic functions and their graphs
- simultaneous equations

Shape, space and measures

Questions involving

- metric units and Imperial units
- constructions
- areas and volumes
- circles
- speed

Questions involving

- plane shapes and their properties
- solid shapes and their properties
- nets
- symmetry

Questions involving

- angles
- bearings and scale drawings
- transformations on a grid
- enlargement
- Pythagoras' theorem
- trigonometry

Handling data

Questions involving

- raw data and tallying
- bar charts and frequency diagrams
- range, mean, median and mode
- pie charts
- line graphs
- conversion graphs
- scatter diagrams

Questions involving

- outcomes of events
- probability

Note: Questions follow the ISEB examination format and are numbered either:

1.   (a)
      (b)
      (c)   where parts of questions are **not** related.

OR

1.   (i)
      (ii)
      (iii) where parts of questions **are** related.

Introduction

The curriculum and the examination syllabus

The mathematics curriculum and the examination syllabus are subject to relatively minor changes or emphases from time to time, whereas the body of mathematical skills and knowledge which teachers consider valuable seems to remain fairly constant.

For completeness, and to allow greater flexibility in the use of this material, some questions included here may be outside the syllabus currently examined, even though they are likely to be within the capability of the majority of students in most schools. It is left to teachers to select questions which they consider appropriate and, in any case, it is assumed that teachers will wish to differentiate according to student abilities.

The material is mostly at National Curriculum levels 5, 6 and 7 but, for completeness, questions cover ideas met in all years up to Year 8.

The contents pages outline the way in which questions have been grouped. This closely follows publications by the Department of Education but the sections within the strands have been numbered for easier reference.

Page edge 'flags' are used to identify the strand and the group within the strand:

Number; **C**alculations; **P**roblems; **A**lgebra; **S**hape, space and measures; **D**ata Handling.

ISEB levels 1, 2 and 3

The majority of students are expected to take the **Level 2** papers.

The current syllabus indicates

- restrictions on the basic syllabus for students taking **Level 1** papers
- additions to the basic syllabus for students taking **Level 3** papers.

In this book

- ■■□ indicates questions (or part questions) appropriate for **Level 2** and **Level 3** examinations only
- ■■■ indicates questions (or part questions) appropriate for **Level 3** examinations only.

Most of the questions are suitable for students taking papers at any level.

It is important to remember that:

- the ISEB Levels are simply the levels of the exam papers attempted and do not necessarily reflect the 'level' of classroom experience or practice, or pupil ability
- in the CE exams, many questions (or part questions) are common to the papers at all three levels

- Level 3 papers contain some (by no means most) questions based upon the extended syllabus.

- some examination topics, such as symmetry, rarely, if ever, lend themselves to 'Level 3' questions.

Using this book

The book has been designed for use by students, under the guidance of a teacher or parent, as a resource for practice of basic skills and recall of knowledge.

Students are expected to produce a personal record of achievement which will prove valuable as an additional revision aid. Worksheets are available to assist with some questions and are indicated by $\boxed{6}$ with the relevant number. These are available from www.galorepark.co.uk. Students are expected to show full working where appropriate and, at all times, to make their method clear to the marker.

It is assumed that, throughout, students will

- make use of estimation skills

- pay attention to the order of operations (BIDMAS or BODMAS)

- use strategies to check the reasonableness of results

- use a calculator **only** when instructed or allowed to do so.

It is strongly recommended that reference is made regularly to the current ISEB Examination Syllabus and to recent past papers.

Whilst this book has been compiled for use by pupils preparing for independent schools entrance exams, it is expected that it will also prove useful for students in state schools and home schoolers.

The questions

Almost all of the questions are modelled on questions from past 13+ Common Entrance papers, using similar wording and mark allocation.

Within each broad group of questions, some grading in difficulty has been attempted. Harder questions may be found towards the end of each grouping. Many of these harder questions will be within the capabilities of most students.

Many questions involve several skills. These questions have not been split but have been placed wherever seemed most appropriate.

The number of questions on a particular topic reflects the frequency with which such questions have appeared in the Common Entrance papers.

Numbers are written in words in the mental strategies sections to reflect the sheets teachers use in examinations.

Calculators

Questions in **N1, N2, C1** and **C2** should be tackled **without** a calculator.

A2, S2, P1 and **D1** – in these sections you should not need to use a calculator.

Questions in **C3** require the use of a suitable calculator.

Questions which involve both calculator and non-calculator parts have the parts clearly indicated.

It is assumed that students will

- be encouraged to tackle all other questions **without** the use of a calculator

- have the opportunity to decide for themselves when the use of a calculator is appropriate and when other methods are more effective.

Number

N1 Properties of numbers

In this section the questions cover the following topics:

● Multiples and factors

● Prime numbers

● Negative numbers

● Place value

● Ordering

● Estimation and approximation

Many questions cover several topics.

In this section the questions must be answered without using a calculator.

1. Write **one positive whole number** in each case.

   (You may use a number more than once if you wish.)

   (a) a factor of 42 (1)

   (b) a prime factor of 45 (1)

   (c) a multiple of 24 (1)

   (d) a prime number between 50 and 60 (1)

   (e) the square of 4 (1)

   (f) the square root of 4 (1)

   (g) the cube of 5 (1)

   (h) the cube root of 8 (1)

2. From the following list of numbers, choose a **different** number for each answer.

   | 4 | 8 | 10 | 18 | 36 | 39 | 47 |

   (i) a perfect square (1)

   (ii) the cube root of 64 (1)

   (iii) a multiple of 13 (1)

   (iv) a prime number (1)

   (v) a factor of 54 (1)

3. Look at the eight directed number cards below.

| $^-5$ | $^-4$ | $^-2$ | $^-1$ | 2 | 5 | 6 | 8 |

(i) What is the sum of all eight cards? (2)

(ii) Choose two cards which have a sum of zero. (1)

(iii) Which two cards give the lowest product? (2)

(iv) Copy the statements below.

    (a) _ + _ = 1 (1)

    (b) _ − _ = 7 (1)

    (c) _ × _ = 4 (2)

    (d) _ ÷ _ = 4 (2)

Using all eight directed number cards once only, fill in the gaps.

4. Find the value of:

(a) (i) $^-4 + 7$ (1)

    (ii) $5 - 3$ (1)

    (iii) $6 - {}^-5$ (1)

    (iv) $8 + {}^-4 - {}^-3$ (2)

(b) (i) $4 \times {}^-3$ (1)

    (ii) $^-5 \times {}^-6$ (1)

    (iii) $(^-2)^3$ (1)

    (iv) $9 \div {}^-3$ (1)

5. (i) Find the value of:

    (a) $18 + 16 \times 3$ (2)

    (b) $(18 + 16) \times 3$ (2)

(ii) Find the difference between your answer to part (i) (a) and your answer to part (i) (b). (1)

6. (a) Calculate:

    (i) $3^2 \times 2^3$ (2)

    (ii) $\sqrt[3]{1000}$ (1)

(b) Write 220 as a product of prime factors, using indices. (3)

7. (a) Find the value of $2 \times 3^2 \times 5 \times 11$ (2)

(b) Express 230 as a product of its prime factors. (3)

(c) Write down the smallest square number which is even and is a multiple of 11 (2)

(d) Write down two prime numbers which have a sum of 42 (2)

8. (a) Write the following numbers in descending order of size,

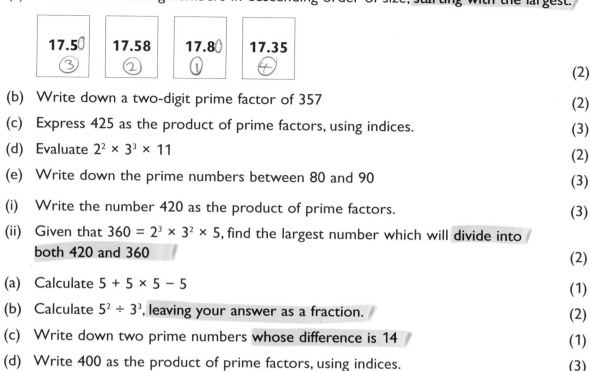

(2)

(b) Write down a two-digit prime factor of 357 (2)

(c) Express 425 as the product of prime factors, using indices. (3)

(d) Evaluate $2^2 \times 3^3 \times 11$ (2)

(e) Write down the prime numbers between 80 and 90 (3)

9. (i) Write the number 420 as the product of prime factors. (3)

(ii) Given that $360 = 2^3 \times 3^2 \times 5$, find the largest number which will divide into both 420 and 360 (2)

10. (a) Calculate $5 + 5 \times 5 - 5$ (1)

(b) Calculate $5^2 \div 3^3$, leaving your answer as a fraction. (2)

(c) Write down two prime numbers whose difference is 14 (1)

(d) Write 400 as the product of prime factors, using indices. (3)

■■□ 11. Arrange the following numbers in order of size, starting with the smallest:

(3)

12. (a) Round:

(i) 545 to the nearest ten (1)

(ii) 1045 to the nearest hundred (1)

(iii) 48.09 to the nearest whole number. (1)

(b) Write:

(i) 30.749 to 1 decimal place (1)

(ii) 0.405 to 2 decimal places (1)

(iii) 209.55 to 3 significant figures (1)

(iv) 0.0509509509… to 3 significant figures. (2)

13. (a) Estimate, to the nearest whole number:

(i) 8.91×4.03 (1)

(ii) $56.2 \div 6.9$ (2)

(b) Estimate, to 1 significant figure:

(i) 10.9×9.9 (1)

(ii) $240.3 \div 7.95$ (2)

■■□ 14. Write the following numbers in decreasing order of size with the largest first:

②	①	③	④
$\frac{5}{9}$	**0.6**	$\frac{27}{50}$	**53%**

55.5   60   54   53

(4)

15. By first writing each number correct to 1 significant figure, estimate the value of

$$\frac{49.5 \times 40.6}{19.85}$$

(3)

■■□ 16. (a) Estimate to one significant figure, showing your working clearly, the value of

$$\frac{297 \times 0.21}{5.9 \times 5.1}$$

(3)

(b) $131 \times 0.295 = 38.645$

Write down the values of:

(i) 131×29.5 (1)

(ii) $38\,645 \div 295$ (2)

(c) Given that

$$\frac{54 \times 3.55}{1.25 \times 560} = 0.273\,857 \text{ to 6 decimal places, find the value, to 3 decimal places, of}$$

$$\frac{540 \times 0.355}{12.5 \times 5.6}$$

(2)

N2 Fractions, decimals, percentages; ratio

In this section the questions cover the following topics:

- Fractions
- Decimals
- Percentages
- Ratio and proportion

Many questions cover several topics.

In this section the questions must be answered without using a calculator.

1. (a) (i) Write the fraction representing 5 parts of a whole containing 9 parts. (1)

    (ii) What fraction of this rectangle has been shaded? (2)

(b) Change the fraction $\frac{4}{5}$ to:

    (i)   an equivalent fraction with denominator 40   (1)

    (ii) a decimal   (1)

    (iii) a percentage.   (1)

2.   (a) Write the fraction $\frac{16}{36}$ in its simplest form (lowest terms).   (1)

    (b) (i)   Write the improper fraction $\frac{7}{4}$ as a mixed number.   (1)

           (ii) Write the mixed number $3\frac{3}{4}$ as an improper fraction.   (1)

    (c) (i)   Write the mixed number $4\frac{3}{5}$ as a decimal.   (2)

           (ii) Write the fraction $\frac{17}{20}$ as a percentage.   (2)

3.   Copy and complete the table below.   (6)

Fraction (in lowest terms)	Decimal	Percentage
$\frac{2}{5}$		%
		24%
	0.35	%

4.   (a) Write down two different fractions which are equivalent to two thirds.   (2)

    (b) Evaluate, giving your answer in cm, 280 mm + 43.8 cm + 1.1 m   (3)

5.   (a) Write 0.48 as a fraction in its lowest terms.   (2)

    (b) Express 45% as a fraction in its lowest terms.   (2)

    (c) Write $\frac{5}{8}$ as a percentage.   (2)

6.   (a) Write 15% as a fraction.   (2)

    (b) Write $\frac{13}{25}$ as a decimal.   (2)

    (c) Calculate 40% of £350   (2)

    (d) Calculate $\frac{4}{5}$ of 6.5 kilometres.   (2)

7.   (a) Evaluate:

    (i) $\frac{3}{4}$ of £4.80   (2)

    (ii) 20% of £45.50   (2)

    (b) Express 20 centimetres as a <u>percentage</u> of 4 metres.   (2)

8. (a) A school has 300 pupils. One day 36 pupils were absent from school attending an athletics tournament.

    (i) What percentage of the 300 pupils was absent that day? (2)

    (ii) What fraction of the 300 pupils was present that day?
          Simplify your answer as much as you can. (2)

    (b) Shanna sees two jackets in a sale.

Jacket A
was **£40**
now
15% off

Jacket B
was **£48**
now $\frac{1}{4}$ off

Shanna buys the jacket with the cheaper sale price.

    (i) Which jacket does Shanna buy? (2)

    (ii) How much change does she get from a £50 note? (2)

9. (a) Last year in Snuffletown there were 60 reported cases of 'flu. This year the number dropped by 35%. How many cases have been reported this year? (2)

    (b) When a farmer digs up 200 kg of carrots, he finds that 10% are rotten.

    (i) What is the mass of the healthy carrots? (1)

    Of the remaining healthy carrots, 10% are too small to sell.

    (ii) What is the mass of healthy carrots which are large enough to sell? (1)

10. (i) When Mr Watchit went to buy a television, VAT (Value Added Tax) was charged at 20%, payable on the basic price. The basic price of the television was £400

    (a) Calculate the VAT payable. (2)

    (b) Calculate the price including VAT. (1)

    (ii) The shop offered Mr Watchit a 5% discount on the total price (including VAT) if he paid by debit card rather than by credit card.
          How much did Mr Watchit pay if he paid by debit card? (3)

11. (i) James bought a rare stamp for £80 at auction and a year later sold it to a dealer, making a 45% profit on his buying price. Calculate his selling price. (2)

    The stamp was then sold by the dealer for £290

    (ii) (a) How much profit did the dealer make on the sale? (1)

    (b) Write the dealer's profit as a percentage of his buying price. (2)

12. On her birthday, Gemma eats $\frac{1}{5}$ of her cake and her brother Ben eats $\frac{3}{10}$ of the cake.

(i) What fraction of the cake is left after Gemma and Ben have eaten their portions? (3)

Gemma shares the remaining cake equally between three friends.

(ii) What fraction of the original cake does each friend receive? (2)

13. (a) What fraction of this diagram has been shaded? (1)

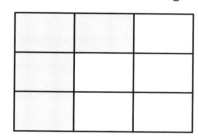

(b) (i) Copy the diagram below and shade part of it to represent the result of the calculation

$$\frac{5}{9} + \frac{1}{9}$$

(1)

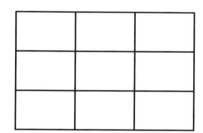

(ii) What fraction, in its simplest form (lowest terms), of the diagram is now not shaded? (2)

■■☐ 14. (a) Calculate $\frac{1}{4} + \frac{3}{5}$ (2)

(b) Aidan, Bill and Caitlin shared a pizza.

Aidan ate $\frac{2}{5}$ of the pizza.

Bill ate $\frac{2}{3}$ of what was left.

(i) What fraction of the whole pizza did Bill eat? (2)

Caitlin ate the rest.

(ii) What fraction of the whole pizza did Caitlin eat? (2)

■■☐ 15. Evaluate the following, giving your answers in their simplest form.

(a) $\frac{6}{5} + \frac{5}{6}$ (2)

(b) $\frac{13}{5} \times \frac{5}{6}$ (2)

(c) $18 \div \frac{12}{5}$ (2)

■■□ 16. Evaluate, simplifying where possible:

(a) $\frac{2}{5} + \frac{1}{3}$ (2)

(b) $1\frac{1}{2} - \frac{1}{3}$ (2)

(c) $\frac{4}{5} \times \frac{15}{16}$ (2)

■■■ (d) $1\frac{3}{4} \div \frac{5}{8}$ (2)

■■■ 17. Evaluate, simplifying where possible:

(a) $4\frac{1}{3} - 3\frac{1}{4} + 2\frac{1}{2}$ (3)

(b) $(4\frac{1}{2} + 2\frac{1}{4}) \times \frac{1}{3}$ (3)

■■■ 18. Evaluate:

(a) $4\frac{3}{5} - 2\frac{1}{4}$ (3)

(b) $3\frac{1}{4} \div 2\frac{1}{5}$ (3)

19. (a) Terry baked a large cake from ingredients which cost £20
She sold the cake, making a profit of 35%
For what price did she sell the cake? (2)

(b) One day, Sam sold 25 burgers for 90 pence each.

(i) How much did the burgers sell for altogether? (2)

The next day he increased the price by 10% but the number of burgers sold fell by 8%

(ii) Did Sam's takings from the sale of burgers increase or decrease and by how much? (4)

20. The diagram below shows dark and milk chocolates in a box.

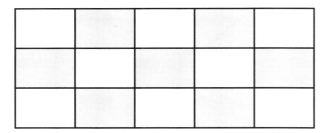

Write the ratio:

(i) number of dark chocolates : total number of chocolates (1)

(ii) number of dark chocolates : number of milk chocolates. (1)

21. The diagram below shows shapes in a box.

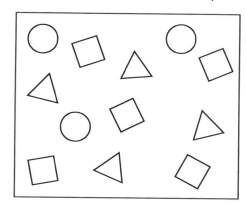

The numbers of the different shapes are in the ratio

    circles   :   triangles   :   squares
      3   :   4   :   5

What is the ratio:
(i)   circles : total number of shapes   (1)
(ii) triangles : squares   (1)
(iii) squares : circles   (1)

■■□ 22. (a) The numbers of ice-creams and drinks sold by Jane are in the ratio 8 : 5

    (i)   On Saturday Jane sold 168 ice-creams.
         How many drinks did she sell?   (2)

    (ii) On Sunday Jane sold a total of 169 ice-creams and drinks.
         How many ice-creams did she sell?   (2)

   (b) A map is drawn to a scale of 1 : 50 000
      How many centimetres on the map represent 5 kilometres on the ground?   (3)

23. (a) Find the value of $\frac{4}{5}$ of £85   (2)

   (b) A recipe for 8 muffins requires 120 grams of flour.
      How much flour will I need for 18 muffins?   (2)

■■□ 24. Gail's packet of mixed nuts contains 140 nuts. The nuts are almonds, Brazil nuts and hazelnuts. 40 of the nuts are almonds.

(i)   Write down, in its simplest form, the ratio of almonds to other nuts.   (2)

Of those nuts which are not almonds, 20% are Brazil nuts and the rest are hazelnuts.

(ii) How many nuts are hazelnuts?   (2)

Gail gives away all the almonds and eats a quarter of the Brazil nuts.

(iii) What fraction of the remaining nuts are Brazil nuts?   (3)

■ ■ □ 25. (i) A road which rises 1 metre for every 20 metres travelled horizontally is said to have a gradient of 1 in 20

This can also be written as a gradient of 5% because $\frac{1}{20}$ is equivalent to 5%.

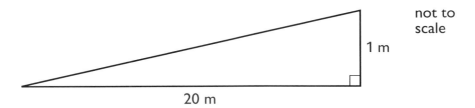

not to scale

1 m

20 m

Write down the percentage equivalents of the following slopes:

(a) 7 in 50 (1)

(b) 1 in 8 (2)

(ii) The diagram below shows a block of wood resting on a 2 metre plank *AB*.

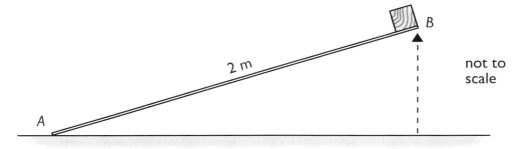

John slowly raises end *B* of the plank, leaving end *A* on the ground. The block of wood starts to slide down the plank when the gradient of the slope reaches 5%. *Approximately* how high above the ground must John lift end *B* before the block starts to slide? (2)

■ ■ ■ 26. (i) Evaluate, giving your answers as mixed fractions:

(a) $2\frac{3}{4} \times \frac{3}{4} - \frac{1}{2}$ (3)

(b) $(\frac{3}{4} + 1\frac{2}{3}) \div \frac{1}{5}$ (3)

(ii) Calculate the difference between your two answers in part (i). (3)

■ ■ ■ 27. Calculate

(i) $3\frac{1}{4} + 2\frac{3}{4}$ (1)

(ii) $3\frac{1}{4} - 2\frac{3}{4}$ (2)

(iii) $3\frac{1}{4} \times 2\frac{3}{4}$ (3)

(iv) $3\frac{1}{4} \div 2\frac{3}{4}$ (4)

Calculations

C1 Mental strategies

In this section the questions **must** be answered:

- **without** using a calculator
- **without** using any measuring instruments
- **without** making any written calculations.

These questions cover all areas of the syllabus; they are **not** grouped by topic or graded in difficulty.

The questions are printed as they would be read, using words rather than numerals in most cases. **Hearing** the questions read by someone else involves remembering the important details. In these questions you have the opportunity to re-read the questions as necessary, which makes life easier in many cases! The questions should be answered as quickly as possible and an average of about **10** seconds should normally be sufficient for each part, or about a minute for each numbered question of 5 parts.

For many questions, a variety of strategies can be used.

1. (a) Find the cost of five DVDs, each costing eleven pounds ninety-nine pence. (1)

    (b) Wendy celebrated her tenth birthday in 2010. In which year was she born? (1)

    (c) Find the value of four to the power of three. (1)

    (d) A prize of two hundred and fifty-six pounds is shared equally between eight people. How much does each person receive? (1)

    (e) Cans of fizzy drink cost forty-nine pence each. A multipack of ten cans costs four pounds fifty pence. How much do I save by buying the multipack rather than ten separate cans? (1)

2. (a) I invest six hundred pounds at three per cent interest per annum. If I do not add or withdraw any money, how much is in my account after one year? (1)

    (b) Sarah swims fifty lengths of a twenty-five metre length swimming pool. How far does she swim? Give your answer in kilometres. (1)

    (c) In a school of four hundred pupils, one hundred and twenty sing in the choir. What is the probability that a pupil selected at random does *not* sing in the choir? (1)

    (d) The cost of going to the cinema is shown.

    | adult £8.50 |
    | child £5.00 |

    How much will it cost for two adults and four children to go to the cinema? (1)

(e) What is the order of symmetry of the shape? (1)

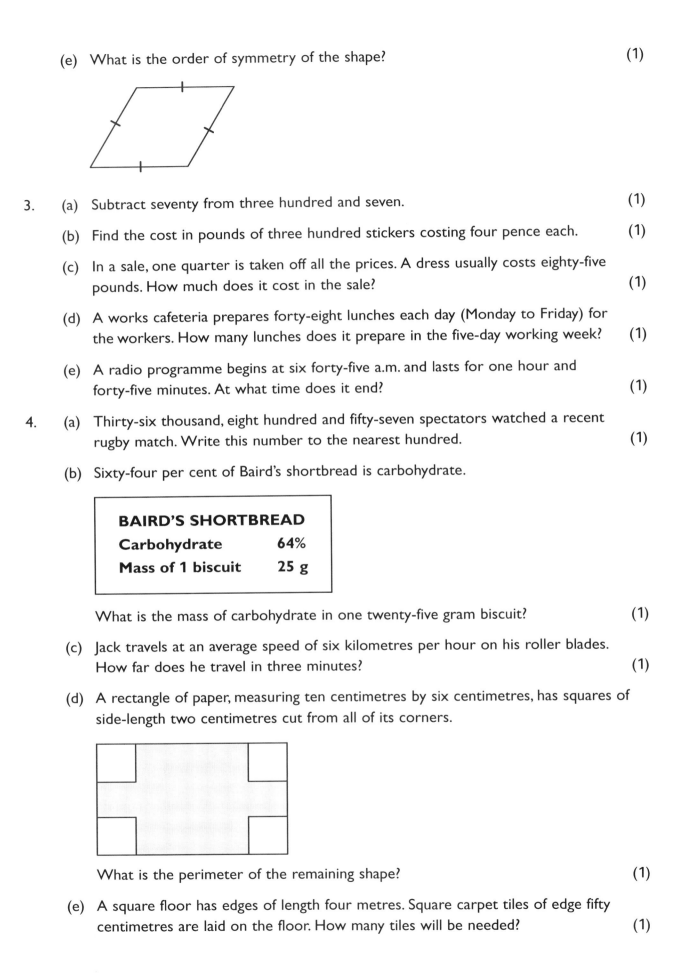

3. (a) Subtract seventy from three hundred and seven. (1)

(b) Find the cost in pounds of three hundred stickers costing four pence each. (1)

(c) In a sale, one quarter is taken off all the prices. A dress usually costs eighty-five pounds. How much does it cost in the sale? (1)

(d) A works cafeteria prepares forty-eight lunches each day (Monday to Friday) for the workers. How many lunches does it prepare in the five-day working week? (1)

(e) A radio programme begins at six forty-five a.m. and lasts for one hour and forty-five minutes. At what time does it end? (1)

4. (a) Thirty-six thousand, eight hundred and fifty-seven spectators watched a recent rugby match. Write this number to the nearest hundred. (1)

(b) Sixty-four per cent of Baird's shortbread is carbohydrate.

BAIRD'S SHORTBREAD
Carbohydrate 64%
Mass of 1 biscuit 25 g

What is the mass of carbohydrate in one twenty-five gram biscuit? (1)

(c) Jack travels at an average speed of six kilometres per hour on his roller blades. How far does he travel in three minutes? (1)

(d) A rectangle of paper, measuring ten centimetres by six centimetres, has squares of side-length two centimetres cut from all of its corners.

What is the perimeter of the remaining shape? (1)

(e) A square floor has edges of length four metres. Square carpet tiles of edge fifty centimetres are laid on the floor. How many tiles will be needed? (1)

5. (a) Subtract fifty-nine from one hundred and twenty. (1)

    (b) Work out seventy percent of three hundred pounds. (1)

    (c) What is the next prime number greater than seventy-three? (1)

    (d) A recipe for a dozen buns requires two hundred and forty grams of flour. How much flour will be required to make nine buns? (1)

    (e) ABCD is a kite with angle D equal to forty degrees.

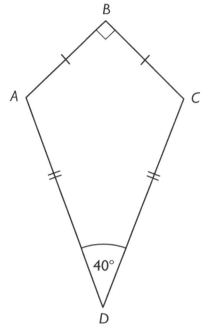

    What is the size of angle C? (1)

6. (a) A fair pentagonal spinner has numbers one to five as shown.

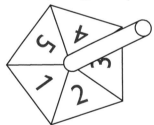

    What is the probability that the spinner lands on a prime number? (1)

    (b) Niall buys a pair of jeans costing twenty-four pounds fifty and a shirt costing eighteen pounds fifty. How much change does he get from a fifty-pound note? (1)

    (c) The population of a village is recorded as three thousand, five hundred and twenty-six. Write this number to the nearest fifty. (1)

    (d) It takes Carole an average of four minutes to read a page of a novel. How many complete pages could she read in an hour and a half? (1)

    (e) The cost of hiring a taxi is made up of two parts. There is a basic charge of two pounds. In addition, each passenger in the taxi pays sixty pence for each mile travelled. What is the total cost for two passengers in a taxi travelling four miles? (1)

13

7.   (a) Write down the number which is double forty-seven.   (1)

    (b) Peter buys a bag of forty-six sweets. He eats nineteen sweets. How many sweets does he have left?   (1)

    (c) Write the number forty thousand and twenty-three in figures.   (1)

    (d) Jo pays seventy-six pence for a small loaf of bread. How much change should she receive from one pound?   (1)

    (e) Write down the number which is the square root of nine hundred.   (1)

8.   (a) In his pocket Felix has only red marbles and blue marbles. If the probability of picking out a red marble is three sevenths, what is the probability of picking out a blue marble?   (1)

    (b) Find the cost of twenty litres of petrol at one hundred and ten point five pence per litre.   (1)

    (c) Divide fifty-six by four and then subtract eight.   (1)

    (d) Oranges cost twenty-eight pence each and apples cost twenty-two pence each. Find the cost of three oranges and three apples.   (1)

    (e) The difference between two numbers is eleven. If the larger number is nine, write down the other number.   (1)

9.   (a) What is the difference between forty-seven and nineteen?   (1)

    (b) Look at the scale. What is the reading shown by the arrow?   (1)

    (c) Multiply forty-one by twelve.   (1)

    (d) Twenty people share four thousand six hundred pounds equally. How much is each person's share?   (1)

    (e) Two point two pounds are equal to one kilogram. Tom weighs 110 pounds. What does he weigh in kilograms?   (1)

10.   (a) The adult bus fare from Threwelli to Soggidog is fourteen pounds. Children travel half-price. What is the total cost for two adults and three children to travel from Threwelli to Soggidog?   (1)

    (b) Calculate the mean of the numbers.   (1)

8	⁻3	4	11	⁻5

    (c) In a box there are four red, seven blue and nine green buttons. Grant picks one button at random. What is the probability that he picks a red button?   (1)

(d) Zac thought of a number, squared it and then divided the result by two. He got seventy-two. What number did he think of? (1)

(e) How many square tiles of side twenty centimetres are needed to cover a rectangular floor which measures three metres by four metres? (1)

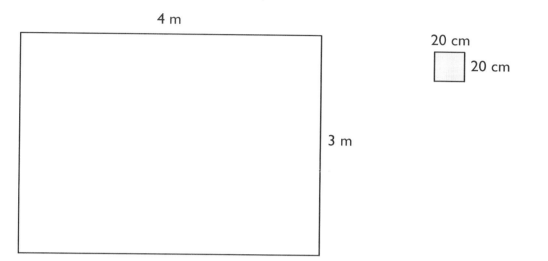

4 m

20 cm

20 cm

3 m

11. (a) A bag of sweets costs eighty-seven pence. What is the cost of three bags of sweets? (1)

(b) How many sides has a nonagon? (1)

(c) Work out four-fifths of eighty. (1)

(d) Write down the square root of one hundred and twenty-one. (1)

(e) What is the value of five plus six plus seven plus eight? (1)

12. (a) How many centimetres are there in four point seven metres? (1)

(b) The temperature in my fridge was negative four degrees Celsius. It is now three degrees lower. What is the temperature now? (1)

(c) What is half of seventy-four minus a third of thirty-nine? (1)

(d) Copy and complete the shape so that it has rotational symmetry of order two. (1)

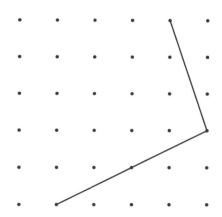

(e) A circle has radius twelve centimetres. Estimate the circumference of the circle. (1)

C2 Written methods

In this section the questions must be answered without using a calculator.

It is expected that all working is clearly set out. This will help you to avoid errors and gain more marks.

For many questions, a variety of strategies can be used.

Remember that in many cases, the correct 'answer' is less important than the 'working'.

An estimate before doing the calculation and a check afterwards will help to eliminate careless errors leading to 'ridiculous' answers.

1.　Evaluate:

    (a)　4.76 + 11.89 　　　　　　　　　　　　　　　　　　(2)

    (b)　10.35 − 4.63 　　　　　　　　　　　　　　　　　　(2)

    (c)　35.7 × 8 　　　　　　　　　　　　　　　　　　　(2)

    (d)　82.8 ÷ 8 　　　　　　　　　　　　　　　　　　　(2)

2.　Evaluate:

    (a)　4.75 + 2.98 　　　　　　　　　　　　　　　　　　(2)

    (b)　4.75 − 2.98 　　　　　　　　　　　　　　　　　　(2)

    (c)　4.75 × 5 　　　　　　　　　　　　　　　　　　　(2)

    (d)　4.75 ÷ 5 　　　　　　　　　　　　　　　　　　　(2)

3.　Calculate:

    (a)　7.48 + 2.59 　　　　　　　　　　　　　　　　　　(2)

    (b)　7.48 − 2.59 　　　　　　　　　　　　　　　　　　(2)

    (c)　25.2 × 7 　　　　　　　　　　　　　　　　　　　(2)

    (d)　25.2 ÷ 7 　　　　　　　　　　　　　　　　　　　(2)

4.　Evaluate:

    (a)　5.08 + 2.9 　　　　　　　　　　　　　　　　　　(1)

    (b)　5.08 − 2.9 　　　　　　　　　　　　　　　　　　(2)

    (c)　5.08 × 2.9 　　　　　　　　　　　　　　　　　　(3)

    (d)　5.08 ÷ 4 　　　　　　　　　　　　　　　　　　　(2)

5.　Find the value of the following:

    (a)　£8.70 + £5.80 　　　　　　　　　　　　　　　　　(2)

    (b)　£8.70 − £5.80 　　　　　　　　　　　　　　　　　(2)

    (c)　£8.70 × 4 　　　　　　　　　　　　　　　　　　　(2)

    (d)　£8.70 ÷ 6 　　　　　　　　　　　　　　　　　　　(2)

6. Calculate:

   (a) 7 + 4 × 5 (1)

   (b) 5 + 8 × (9 − 3) (3)

7. Evaluate:

   (a) (i) 23.8 × 7 (2)

       (ii) 23.8 × 0.07 (1)

   (b) (i) 23.8 ÷ 7 (2)

       (ii) 23.8 ÷ 0.07 (2)

8. Evaluate:

   (a) 293 g + 2.09 kg

       (i) in grams (2)

       (ii) in kilograms (1)

   (b) 47.4 cm − 59 mm

       (i) in centimetres (2)

       (ii) in metres (1)

9. (a) Calculate the total cost of buying 16 rugby shirts at £29.45 each. (3)

   (b) When 16 people go for a meal, the total cost of the meals is £124.80
   What is the cost of each meal if they are all the same price? (3)

10. Evaluate the following:

    (a) 109.39 + 10.87 (2)

    (b) 109.39 − 10.87 (2)

    (c) 2.76 × 0.24 (2)

    (d) 2.76 ÷ 0.24 (2)

11. Calculate:

    (a) the sum of 89.9 and 3.07 (1)

    (b) the difference between 67 and 6.7 (1)

    (c) 2.94 × 0.8 (2)

    (d) 5.6 ÷ 0.8 (2)

C2

C3 Calculator methods

In this section a calculator is essential for most questions.

In a few questions a calculator should be used for only part of the question and the non-calculator part is clearly indicated by this symbol

In most cases it is important to write more than just the 'answer'. Say what you are doing.

Remember that the calculator will respond faultlessly to the instructions given to it so it is very important that you give it the appropriate instructions!

It is a good idea to know roughly what the calculator answer is likely to be before you start and a check after the calculation is always a good idea.

Remember that different calculators work in different ways and you should have absolute confidence in your own calculator and your ability to use it.

Unless instructed otherwise, write all the figures shown in the calculator display first and then write the answer to **3 significant figures**.

1. Tina's calculator display is shown here, after she has done a multiplication.

   ┌─────────────────┐
   │ *10.4974*   │
   └─────────────────┘

   (i) Write the number shown in the display correct to two decimal places. (1)

   (ii) Write the number shown in the display correct to one significant figure. (2)

   (iii) Which number did Tina multiply by 1.46? (2)

■■□ 2. $\dfrac{58.9}{4.9 \times 8.1}$

   (i) **Without using a calculator**, and showing all your working,

   (a) rewrite the calculation shown above, giving each number correct to one significant figure (2)

   (b) evaluate your answer to part (i) (a). (1)

   (ii) (a) Now, using a calculator and writing down all the figures displayed, evaluate

   $\dfrac{58.9}{4.9 \times 8.1}$ (2)

   (b) Write your answer to part (ii) (a) correct to three significant figures. (1)

   (c) Write your answer to part (ii) (a) correct to three decimal places. (1)

3. Annie buys a 600 gram jar of jam costing £2.46 and a 400 gram jar of the same jam costing £1.84

   (i) Find the cost of 100 grams of jam in

   (a) the 600 gram jar (1)

   (b) the 400 gram jar. (2)

18

Annie pours the contents of the two jars into an empty pot and mixes them.

(ii) What is the cost of 100 grams of the jam mixture in the pot? (2)

4. (i) Writing down all the figures on your calculator, find the value of
$(39.5 \times 17.3) + (18.6 \times 60.4)$ (2)

(ii) Write your answer to part (i) to two significant figures. (1)

5. (i) Writing down all the figures shown on your calculator, find the value of
$$\frac{30.9}{7.3 + 12.8}$$ (2)

(ii) Write your answer to part (i) correct to 3 significant figures. (1)

(iii) Write your answer to part (i) correct to 3 decimal places. (1)

6. (i) Use your calculator to find the value of $\dfrac{107.8 - 17.9}{9.45 \times 0.57}$ giving all the figures on your calculator display. (2)

(ii) Write your answer to part (i) correct to

(a) three decimal places (1)

(b) one significant figure. (1)

7. (a) (i) Writing down all the figures shown on your calculator, evaluate
$$\frac{509 - 4.73}{0.94 \times 0.183}$$ (2)

(ii) Write your answer to part (a) (i) correct to the nearest tenth. (1)

(iii) Write your answer to part (a) (i) correct to the nearest thousand. (1)

(b) **Without using a calculator**, and showing all your working, first write each number correct to one significant figure, and then estimate the value of
$$\frac{804 \times 0.19}{11.3 \times 7.9}$$ (3)

8. (a) (i) Writing down all the figures shown on your calculator, evaluate
$$\frac{49.7}{5.2 - 4.95}$$ (2)

(ii) Write your answer to part (a) (i) correct to two significant figures. (1)

(b) Writing down all the figures shown on your calculator, evaluate
$$\frac{20.8}{0.8 \times 1.3}$$ (2)

(c) (i) Writing down all the figures shown on your calculator, evaluate $\sqrt{\dfrac{531}{122}}$ (2)

(ii) Write your answer to part (c) (i) correct to the nearest tenth. (1)

C3

Solving problems

P1 Reasoning about numbers or shapes

The questions in this section cover many areas of the syllabus.

You will:

● make use of your knowledge and experience

● make observations

● find it helpful to ask questions 'What if …?'

Questions should, as far as possible, be answered without the use of a calculator. Questions where the use of a calculator is recommended or essential are indicated by 🖩

For many questions, a variety of strategies can be used.

1. The largest of three consecutive whole numbers is represented by the letter n.

    (i)   Write down the previous two whole numbers in terms of n.   (2)

    (ii) The sum of these three whole numbers is 54
          Form an equation in n and solve it to find n.   (3)

    (iii) Which is the smallest of the three consecutive numbers?   (1)

2. I have four ordinary dice.

    I roll the dice and each one shows a **different** score on its top face.
    The sum of all four scores is 18
    What is the product of the four scores?   (4)

3. A sheet of card measuring 12 cm by 10 cm has
    the letter T cut out, with the dimensions shown
    in the diagram.

    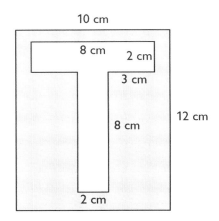

Find:

(i)   the area of the letter T   (4)

(ii) the area of card remaining.   (2)

4.   The diagram shows a tile measuring 20 cm by 10 cm.

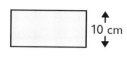

Tiles this size are used to make patterns of varying lengths but all 20 cm wide.

Patterns of lengths 10 cm and 20 cm can only be:

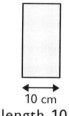 

length 10 cm   length 20 cm
one pattern   two patterns

Patterns of length 30 cm can be:

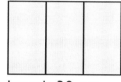 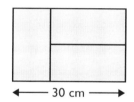 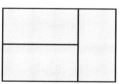

length 30 cm
three patterns

(i)   Draw three possible patterns of length 40 cm.   (3)

(ii)   Draw all possible patterns of length 50 cm.   (4)

(iii) Use your answers and any further investigation to complete the table below.   (4)

Length of pattern	Number of possible patterns
10 cm	1
20 cm	2
30 cm	
40 cm	
50 cm	
60 cm	

P1

21

■ ■ □ 5. (a) The diagram shows a regular hexagon.

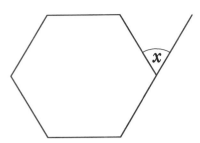

Calculate:

(i)   the size of an exterior angle of the hexagon, marked x (1)

(ii) the size of an interior angle of the hexagon (1)

(iii) the sum of the interior angles of the hexagon. (1)

(b) The hexagon below is not regular, but has two lines of symmetry.

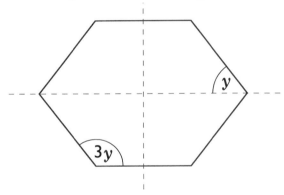

Form an equation in y and solve it to find the value of y. (4)

■ ■ ■ 6. Hamish has an unknown number of marbles which he calls h. Debbie has seven marbles.

(i)   Hamish gives Debbie five of his marbles.

(a) How many marbles does Debbie have now? (1)

(b) Write an expression in terms of h for the number of marbles which Hamish has now. (2)

(ii) Hamish and Debbie lose three marbles each.

(a) How many does Debbie have now? (1)

(b) Write an expression for the number of marbles which Hamish has now. (1)

(c) Write down and simplify an expression for the total number of marbles they have now. (2)

(iii) Hamish and Debbie put all their marbles on a tray and share them equally. Debbie now has the same number of marbles as she had at the start!

Use this information and your answer to (ii) (c) to find out how many marbles Hamish had at the start. (2)

22

7.   The factors of the number 35 are 1, 5, 7 and 35

When added together, they form a 'factor total' of 48

$$1 + 5 + 7 + 35 = 48$$

(i)   Find the factor total of

(a)   34   (1)

(b)   36   (2)

(ii) Find another number between 30 and 40 which has a factor total of 48   (3)

8.   If $4x = 3y$, find:

(i)   the value of y when $x = 18$ (2)

(ii) the value of x when $y = 18$ (2)

(iii) the ratio of y to x.   (2)

9. 2×999 is 1998

$\frac{2}{1001}$ written as a decimal is 0.**001 998** 001 998 ...

This is a recurring decimal with six digits in the repeating section.

You may use your calculator for this question.

(i)   (a)   Write down the value of 3×999 (1)

(b)   Write $\frac{3}{1001}$ as a recurring decimal.   (2)

(ii) (a)   Write down the value of 7×999 (1)

(b)   Write $\frac{7}{1001}$ as a recurring decimal.   (2)

(iii) Considering the six-digit repeating sections in the three recurring decimals, for example 0.**001 998** for $\frac{2}{1001}$, what do you notice about

(a)   the first and second digits   (1)

(b)   the third digit   (1)

(c)   the fourth digit   (1)

(d)   the fifth digit   (1)

(e)   the sixth digit?   (1)

(iv) Considering fractions $\frac{n}{1001}$, **where $n < 11$**, write an expression in terms of n for

(a)   the third digit   (2)

(b)   the sixth digit.   (2)

10. (i) Study the following sequence of numbers. Copy the table and continue the pattern by filling in the blanks. (5)

$3^2 - 0^2 =$	$9 - 0 = 9$	(3×3)
$4^2 - 1^2 =$	$16 - 1 = 15$	(3×5)
$5^2 - 2^2 =$	$25 - 4 =$	
$6^2 - 3^2 =$	$- = 27$	
$7^2 - 4^2 =$	$- =$	
$8^2 - 5^2 =$	$- =$	
$9^2 - 6^2 =$	$- =$	

(ii) What do you notice about the results of the subtractions? (2)

(iii) Without using a calculator, find the value of $100^2 - 97^2$, explaining how you do this. (3)

11. The sequence 1, 2, 3, 6, 11, 20, 37, 68, ... starting with 1, 2, 3 is formed by adding the last three terms to obtain the next one.

For example
$1 + 2 + 3 = 6$
$2 + 3 + 6 = 11$
$3 + 6 + 11 = 20$
$6 + 11 + 20 = 37$ and so on.

(i) Write the next three terms of the sequence after 68 (3)

A, B, C and D are four consecutive terms in the sequence.

(ii) Consider the case when A = 2, B = 3, C = 6 and D = 11

Evaluate:

(a) A + D (1)

(b) B + C (1)

(c) (A + D) − (B + C) (1)

(iii) Repeat part (ii) for a different group of four consecutive terms.

(a) A + D (1)

(b) B + C (1)

(c) (A + D) − (B + C) (1)

(iv) Consider a group of four consecutive terms algebraically.

If A = a, B = b, C = c, write expressions in terms of a, b and c for:

(a) D (1)

(b) A + D (1)

24

(c) B + C   (1)

(d) (A + D) − (B + C)   (1)

(e) Comment on your results.   (2)

■■□ 12. x is a number.

(i) Write down expressions for:

(a) the square of the number   (1)

(b) a quarter of the number.   (1)

The square of the number, divided by a quarter of the number, is 64

(ii) Form, and simplify, an equation in x and solve it to find the number.   (3)

13. Sophie and Sam are trying to find two integers to solve a puzzle.

The numbers:

•   add up to give 60 exactly

•   multiply to give a product which rounds to 850 to the nearest ten.

Sophie's first suggestion is 17 and 43 because 17 + 43 = 60, but the product 17 × 43 is 731 which rounds to 730 to the nearest ten.

Sam's first suggestion is 29 and 31

(i) Find the product of 29 and 31   (1)

(ii) Using trial and improvement, and **showing all your working**, find the pair of integers which will solve the puzzle.   (3)

14. The numbers x, y and z are all positive integers.

y is the smaller of two **even** numbers x and y.

(i) Using the words **odd** or **even**, what can you say about:

(a) $x + y$ (1)

(b) $x - y$ (1)

(c) xy?   (1)

z is an **odd** number.

(ii) Using the words **odd** or **even**, what can you say about:

(a) $x + z$ (1)

(b) xz?   (1)

z is a factor of y.

(iii) Is $\frac{y}{z}$ odd or even?   (1)

The product xyz is 144 and the sum $x + y + z$ is 17

(iv) Find the values of x, y and z.   (3)

15. A square with area **16 cm²** is drawn on the centimetre square dotted grid below.

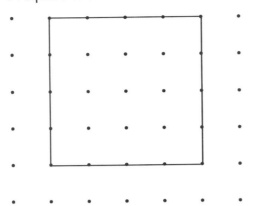

(i) On your worksheet draw examples of the following shapes, all with:

- vertices on grid dots

- area **16 cm²**

(a) a parallelogram (1)

(b) a kite (2)

(c) an isosceles triangle. (2)

(ii) Draw the following shapes, all with:

- vertices on grid dots

- perimeter **16 cm**

(a) a rectangle (1)

(b) a parallelogram (3)

(c) an isosceles triangle. (3)

16. Nine boys, numbered 1 to 9, sit at the vertices of a large regular nonagon drawn on the floor. They play a ball-throwing game.

Boy 1 always starts with the ball.

(i) The ball is thrown from boy to boy, **clockwise** round the nonagon, missing out one boy each time, so boy 1 throws to boy 3, boy 3 throws to boy 5 and so on.

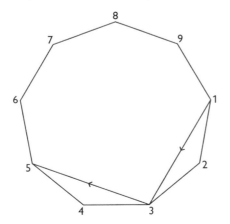

Complete the diagram above until boy 1 receives the ball again. (2)

(ii) In a second game the ball is thrown missing out two boys each time, so boy 1 throws to boy 4, boy 4 throws to boy 7 and so on.

Complete this diagram for the second game. (2)

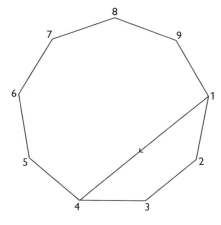

(iii) In a third game the ball is thrown missing out three boys each time.

Complete this diagram for the third game. (2)

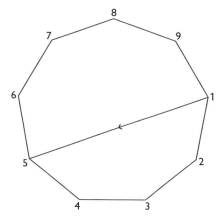

(iv) In a fourth game, boy 1 throws to boy 3 (missing out one boy), boy 3 throws to boy 6 (missing out two boys), boy 6 throws to boy 1 (missing out 3 boys) and then boy 1 throws to boy 6 (missing out 4 boys), and so on.

(a) Complete this diagram for another four throws. (2)

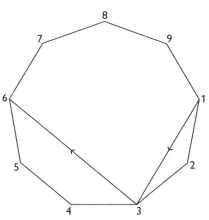

(b) Complete this list of boys who will throw the ball:

1   3   6   1   6   _   _   _   _ (4)

17. Amy is investigating what happens when she applies a rule to a number.

Amy's rule:

> *If the number is*
> - *even, divide it by two*
> - *odd, add 1.*

For example, starting with 67

> 67 is odd so we add 1
> 68 is even so we divide it by 2
> 34 is even so we divide it by 2
> 17 is odd so we add 1
> 18 is even so we divide it by 2
> 9 is a single digit, so we have finished.

We can write this in shorthand as:

$67 \rightarrow 68 \rightarrow 34 \rightarrow 17 \rightarrow 18 \rightarrow 9$

This is a **five-stage** process leading to 9

(i) Write the shorthand process for

    (a) 48   (1)

    (b) 45   (1)

Amy has studied all of the two-digit numbers from 10 to 99

The numbers which lead to 5 are:

A		B	C
		10	(one number)
19	to	20	(two numbers)
37	to	40	(four numbers)
73	to	80	(eight numbers)

(ii) What do you notice about the sequence of numbers in

    (a) column B   (1)

    (b) column A?   (2)

Amy now applies the same rule to three-digit numbers.

(iii) Copy the table below and replace a, b and c with numbers. (3)

A		B	C
	10 (one number)		
19	to	20	(two numbers)
37	to	40	(four numbers)
73	to	80	(eight numbers)
a	to	b	(c numbers)

(iv) Apply the rule to a and b and at least one number between a and b to see if your answer to part (iii) was correct. (3)

Note: You might like to carry out further investigations using this rule.

You may be surprised to learn that the two-digit numbers which lead to 6 are:

A		B	C
11	to	12	(two numbers)
21	to	24	(four numbers)
41	to	48	(eight numbers)
81	to	96	(sixteen numbers)

Without doing any calculations, could you write a table, as above, for the two-digit numbers which lead to 7 or 8 or 9?

18. Paul is investigating what happens when he applies a rule over and over again to a two-digit number.

Paul's rule:

> *Add the product of the digits to the sum of the digits.*

For example,

> $36 \rightarrow 27$ (since $3 \times 6 + 3 + 6$ is 27)
> $27 \rightarrow 23$ (since $2 \times 7 + 2 + 7$ is 23) and then
> $23 \rightarrow 11$
> $11 \rightarrow 3$

This could be written in the shorter version:

$36 \rightarrow 27 \rightarrow 23 \rightarrow 3$

Paul applies the rule over and over again until he reaches a single-digit number. Then he stops.

(i) Follow Paul's rule starting with:

(a) 53 (1)

(b) 81 (1)

(c) 76 (1)

(d) 18 (1)

(ii) What do you notice about your answers to (i)(b) and (i)(d)? (1)

(iii) Follow Paul's rule starting with:

(a) 29 (1)

(b) 59 (1)

(c) 95 (1)

(iv) What do all three numbers in part (iii) have in common? (1)

Paul calls numbers like those in part (iii) 'magic numbers'.

(v) Find four magic numbers between 30 and 45 inclusive (numbers which do not lead to a single-digit number). (4)

(vi) Use your knowledge so far to write down a magic number between 70 and 80 (2)

■■■ 19. Tom thought of a positive integer. He squared the number, multiplied the result by 3, subtracted 12 times his original number and got 351

Showing your method clearly, find Tom's original number? (6)

■■■ 20. A **palindromic number** is one which reads the same backwards and forwards. For example, 66, 747, 3663 and 21312 are all palindromic numbers.

There are just ten **palindromic prime numbers** below 500

(i) Copy the list below and fill in the missing palindromic primes. (5)

11   ___   131   ___   181   ___   313   ___   373   ___

(ii) Explain briefly why:

(a) 11 is the only two-digit palindromic prime (1)

(b) there are no palindromic primes between 200 and 300 (1)

(c) there are no palindromic primes between 400 and 700 (2)

(d) 707 is not prime (1)

(e) 717 is not prime (1)

(iii) Make a suggestion for the smallest 4 digit palindromic prime. (2)

You might like to carry out further investigations in your spare time.

● *Can you find a number which leads to*

(i) 9   *(ii) 7*   *(iii) 5*   *(iv) 1?*

● *Can you find a number which leads to*

(i) 2   *(ii) 8*   *(iii) 6*   *(iv) 4?*

● *How many magic numbers are there?*

P2 Real-life mathematics

In this section many of the questions are concerned to some extent with money or with fractions, decimals and percentages.

The real-life situations may include:

- shopping – money, discounts
- cooking and baking – recipes
- eating and diets – calories
- medicines and health – measures
- growth – measurement, line graphs
- exercise and sports – times, speeds, scores
- holidays and travel – driving, exchange rates
- planning events – hiring equipment, fundraising
- gardening – weed killing, filling a pond
- DIY tasks – building a shed, decorating a room
- business and banking – VAT, profit and loss, interest rates
- design – tessellations, symmetry
- exploring – maps, scales
- model-making – scales, nets
- puzzles.

P2

In this section the questions should be answered without using a calculator wherever possible. Questions where the use of a calculator is recommended or essential are indicated by 🖩

1. (a) Aaron bought 11 badges costing £1.99 each.
        How much did he spend? (2)

    (b) (i)   Samantha bought 4 CDs, 3 costing £6.99 each and the other costing £8.49
              What was the total amount that Samantha spent? (2)

         (ii) How much change should Samantha receive from a £50 note? (2)

    (c) Miss Jones purchased 18 identically priced theatre tickets for her class, at a
        total cost of £207
        What was the cost of each ticket? (2)

2. Barry and Sylvia visit a water garden where there are two rectangular ponds. The ponds
    have the **same perimeter**, but they have different areas.

    Barry walks round one pond which is 16 m long and 12 m wide.

    (i) (a) How far does Barry walk to make one complete circuit of the pond? (1)

         (b) What is the area of this pond? (1)

Sylvia walks round the other pond which is 17.5 m long.

   (ii) (a)   What is the width of this pond?   (1)

         (b)   What is the area of this pond?   (3)

3.   (a)   There are 24 children in Sandra's class.
Two thirds of them are in the orchestra and half of those play the violin.
What fraction of the whole class play the violin in the orchestra?   (2)

    (b)   Bobbie and Clare divide a bar of chocolate so that Bobbie has a quarter of the bar and Clare has a third of the bar.
What fraction of the bar of chocolate remains after Bobbie and Clare have both had their share?   (2)

    (c)   A box of *Doggiebikkies* contains 48 biscuits. Mr Noportuniti shares the biscuits from the box between his dogs. There are enough biscuits for each dog to receive six and there are a few biscuits left.

         (i)   How many dogs does Mr Noportuniti have?   (1)

         (ii)   How many biscuits are left?   (1)

4.   (i)   Copy and complete the shopping list below.   (3)

> 5 kg of potatoes at 45 pence per kg cost _ pence
> 4 kg of carrots at _ pence per kg cost £1.96
> _ kg of leeks at 73 pence per kg cost £2.19

    (ii)   Calculate the total mass in kilograms of the vegetables.   (1)

    (iii)   Calculate the total cost, in pounds, of the vegetables.   (2)

    (iv)   Calculate, to the nearest penny, the mean cost per kilogram of the vegetables.   (2)

5.   Gina is baking 36 buns for a party. Following a recipe, she weighs out the following ingredients: 960 g flour, 0.9 kg sugar, 1.2 kg margarine and 180 g cocoa powder.

    (i)   What is the total mass, in grams, of these ingredients?   (2)

To these ingredients, Gina adds 6 eggs and 1.2 litres of water.

Tom uses the same recipe to make 48 buns. He needs to work out the quantities to use.

    (ii)   Calculate the following for Tom:

         (a)   the number of millilitres of water   (2)

         (b)   the number of eggs   (2)

         (c)   the mass of flour   (2)

         (d)   the mass of margarine.   (2)

6. Two electrical stores are having sales.

   (i) In *Switchiton*, a flat screen TV, originally priced at £490, has the price reduced by 20%. What does it cost in the sale? (2)

   (ii) In *Electrics4U*, the same flat screen TV, originally marked at £500, is reduced to £405

        (a) How much do I save by buying it in the sale? (1)

        (b) What is the percentage discount on the marked price? (2)

7. The wrapper of each *Jupiter* chocolate bar carries one token.

   Twins Anne and Belinda collect these tokens. Anne has 7 and Belinda has 5

   (i) The twins now buy more *Jupiter* bars.

        (a) Anne buys x *Jupiter* bars. Write down, in terms of x, the total number of tokens that Anne has now. (1)

        (b) Belinda buys twice as many bars as Anne has just bought. Write down, in terms of x, the total number of tokens that Belinda has now. (1)

   Belinda now has 3 more tokens than Anne.

   (ii) Write down an equation relating the number of tokens each girl has now. (2)

   (iii) Solve your equation to find x. (2)

   The twins exchange some of their tokens at the shop for two more *Jupiter* bars and they have 3 tokens left between them.

   (iv) How many tokens are exchanged for one *Jupiter* bar? (2)

■■□ 8. (a) The speed of the ball in Sancho's tennis serve was measured as 175 km/h.

        (i) Convert this speed to metres per second, giving your answer correct to the nearest 5 metres per second. (3)

   8 kilometres is approximately equal to 5 miles.

        (ii) Using this conversion rate, calculate the speed of the ball in miles per hour, giving your answer to the nearest 10 miles per hour. (2)

   (b) Sheila cycles at a steady speed of 12 km/h.
   She left home at 09:45 to cycle the 24 kilometres to her aunt's house. Unfortunately, she had to stop for 55 minutes to mend a puncture.
   At what time did she reach her aunt's house? (4)

9. (a) John saws 195 cm from a 2.4 m length of wood.
   How many centimetres are left? (2)

   (b) 34 bus tickets for a trip to Blackpool cost £510
   How much did each ticket cost? (4)

10. A paperback book *Ghosts* containing 300 pages (including the preliminary pages and the cover) is 2.4 cm thick.

   (i) How many copies of *Ghosts* could be fitted side by side on a bookshelf which is 1.2 metres long? (2)

   A similar book, *Witches* contains 400 pages.

   (ii) (a) What is the thickness of this book? (2)

   (b) How many copies of *Witches* could fit onto a 1.2 metre shelf? (3)

11. Shanna wonders if there is a connection between forearm length (from elbow to fingertip) and hand area.

Hand area

Forearm length

The measurements of nine of Shanna's friends are recorded in the table below.

Forearm length (cm)	40	37	42	41	38	44	39	42	40
Hand area (cm²)	110	104	115	109	106	117	112	112	114

   (i) For the results in the table find:

   (a) the range of forearm lengths (1)

   (b) the range of hand areas (1)

   (c) the median forearm length (1)

   (d) the median hand area. (1)

   (ii) Plot the results in the table on a copy of the grid opposite. (3)

   (iii) What type of correlation, if any, is shown by these results? (2)

   (iv) (a) Draw a line of best fit. (1)

   (b) Draw a line on each side of your line of best fit and parallel to it, so that all of the plotted points fall within the area between the two lines. (2)

   Shanna's own forearm length is 36 cm.

   (v) Suggest:

   (a) the minimum (1)

   (b) the maximum (1)

   value which you might expect for the area of Shanna's hand.

   The outline of Shanna's hand is drawn on the centimetre square grid on page 36.

   (vi) Find, as accurately as possible, the area of Shanna's hand. (3)

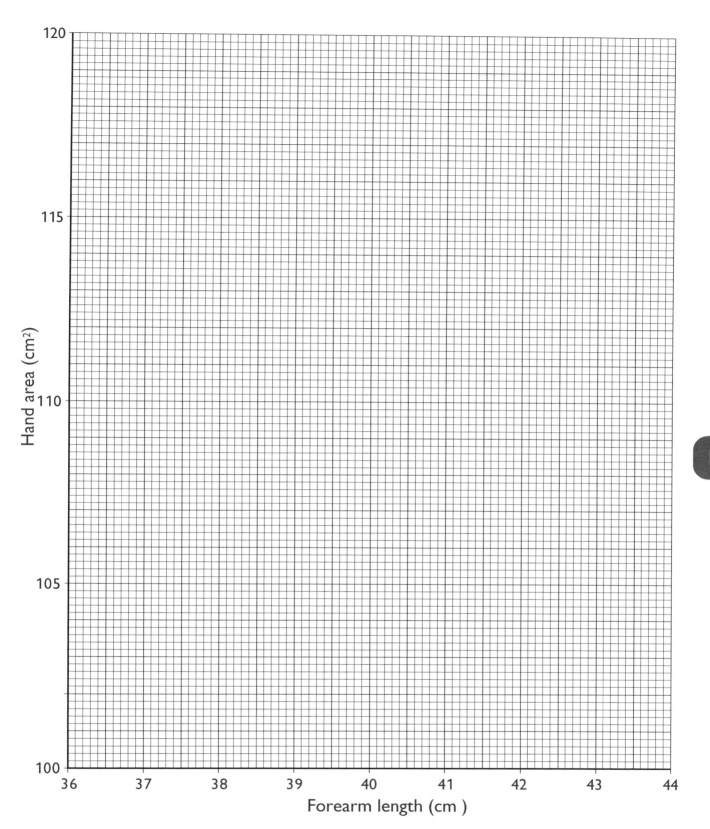

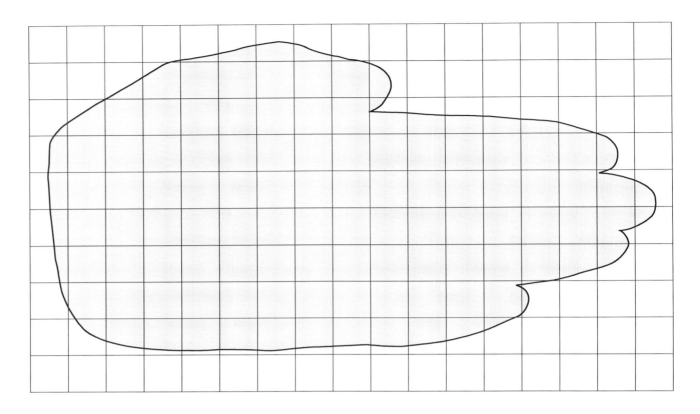

12. Ian's car uses 60 litres of petrol to travel 300 miles.

    (i)   How many miles can the car travel on 50 litres of petrol?   (2)

    (ii) How many litres of petrol would Ian need for a journey of 420 miles?   (2)

When full, the petrol tank in Ian's car holds 64 litres of petrol.
Ian sets off, with a full tank of petrol, on a 420 mile journey.
Ian always refills the petrol tank when it is a quarter full.

    (iii) After approximately how many miles should Ian stop for petrol?   (2)

    (iv) How many litres of fuel will remain in the tank when he reaches his destination? (2)

13. Hannah and Charles have been given a packet of stamps.

Hannah takes exactly $\frac{1}{3}$ of the stamps. Then Charles takes exactly $\frac{3}{4}$ of the stamps remaining.

    (i)   What fraction of the original number of stamps has been taken by Hannah and Charles?   (2)

    (ii) What fraction of the original number of stamps is left in the packet?   (1)

There is a label on the packet.

> *This packet contains between 50 and 55 stamps.*

    (iii) How many stamps were in the packet which Hannah and Charles were given?   (2)

    (iv) How many more stamps did Charles take than Hannah?   (2)

14. In a maths exam, candidates could be awarded one of five grades: A, B, C, D or E.

$\frac{2}{5}$ of the candidates were awarded A or B grades and a quarter of those were A grades.

(i) What fraction of the total number of candidates had:

    (a) A grades (1)

    (b) B grades? (1)

(ii) What fraction of the candidates had C, D or E grades? (1)

Of the candidates who did not achieve A or B grades, three quarters gained C grades.

(iii) What fraction of the total number of candidates achieved C grades? (2)

The number of candidates was more than 70 but less than 90

(iv) How many candidates took the examination? (2)

5 candidates were awarded D grades.

(v) Complete this table of the numbers of candidates who achieved the different grades. (3)

Grade	A	B	C	D	E
Number of candidates				5	

P2

15. In January 2009 there were 420 students at Winterfields School.

The ratio of boys to girls was 6 : 4

(i) How many boys were at the school in January 2009? (2)

By September that year, the number of girls had increased by 32 and the number of boys had decreased by 2

(ii) How many students were at the school in September? (1)

(iii) What was the ratio of boys to girls in September? Give your answer in its simplest form. (2)

(iv) What fraction of the students in September were girls? (2)

(v) What percentage (to the nearest 1%) of the students in September were boys? (2)

16. Stephen's motor scooter uses 12 litres of petrol to travel 96 kilometres.

If the motor scooter uses petrol at a constant rate, find:

(i) how far Stephen can travel on 1 litre of petrol (1)

(ii) how many litres he would use to travel 120 kilometres (1)

(iii) how many kilometres he could travel on a full tank of 18 litres of fuel. (1)

Stephen travelled 432 kilometres one weekend.

(iv) How many litres of petrol did he use? (2)

Petrol costs 124.9 pence per litre.

(v) What was the cost, to the nearest 50 pence, of the petrol? (3)

■■□ 17. The diagram shows a circular cake of diameter 28 cm and depth 7 cm.

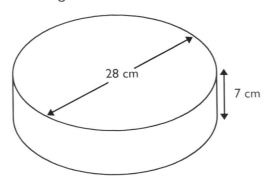

28 cm

7 cm

Take the value of π to be $\frac{22}{7}$

A frill is placed round the circumference of the cake. There is a 2 cm overlap where the ends of the frill are joined.

(i) Calculate the length of the frill, giving your answer to the nearest centimetre. (3)

(ii) Calculate the area of the top of the cake. (3)

(iii) Calculate the volume of the cake. (2)

The cake fits snugly into a box in the shape of a cuboid.

(iv) Calculate the volume of the empty box. (2)

■■□ 18. (a) Ed's cycle has wheels with a circumference of 1.4 metres.

(i) How far will Ed have cycled if a wheel makes 100 revolutions? (1)

(ii) How many complete revolutions will a wheel make when Ed cycles 1 kilometre? (1)

(b) A one pound coin has a diameter of 22.5 mm and a mass of 9.5 grams.

One million pound coins are placed touching in a straight line.

(i) How long will the line be? (2)

(ii) What would be the mass of a million pound coins? (2)

19. The diagram below represents a square garden pond of side 4 metres.

4 m

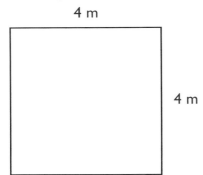

4 m

(i)   Calculate the surface area of the pond. (1)

The water in the pond has a standard depth of 30 cm.

(ii) Calculate the volume of water in the pond. (2)

A path of width 50 cm is made round the pond as shown in the diagram below.

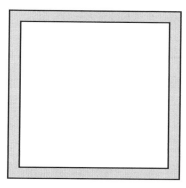

(iii) Calculate the area of the path. (3)

■■□ 20.   Take π to be $\frac{22}{7}$ in this question.

(i)   Calculate the area of a circle with radius 7 cm. (3)

A square tile with sides of 28 cm has semicircular arcs of radius 7 cm drawn inside, as shown in the diagram below.

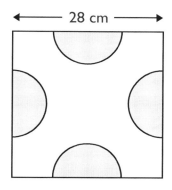

← 28 cm →

P2

(ii) Find the area of:

   (a) the square tile (1)

   (b) the total area of the grey parts (2)

   (c) the area of the white part. (2)

(iii) What percentage of the tile is grey? (2)

21. An open box is made from a rectangular sheet of card measuring x cm by 30 cm.

Squares of side 5 cm are removed from the corners, as shown, to make the net.

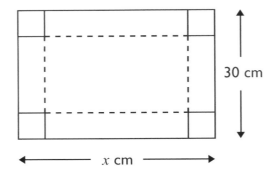

30 cm

x cm

The card is folded along the dotted lines to make the box.

(i) What is the height of the box? (1)

(ii) Write down, in terms of x, an expression for:

   (a) the area of the base of the box (2)

   (b) the surface area of the inside of the box. (4)

The area of the base of the box is 760 cm².

(iii) Calculate:

   (a) the value of x (2)

   (b) the total surface area of the inside of the box. (2)

22. An Ordnance Survey map has a scale of 1 : 50 000

(i) (a) How many metres on the ground are represented by 1 centimetre on the map? (2)

   (b) Write your answer to part (a) in kilometres. (1)

Joe and Andrea are on a walking holiday.

(ii) Joe finds that the distance, on the map, between their present position and a bridge they need to cross is 4.5 centimetres.

What distance, in kilometres, must they walk ('as the crow flies') to reach the bridge? (2)

On this walk, Joe and Andrea move at an average speed of 5 km/h.

(iii) How long will it take them to reach the bridge? (3)

■■□ 23. Arthur collects rainwater from the roof of his shed in a cylindrical tank.

The tank has height 1.5 metres and area of cross-section 1 m².

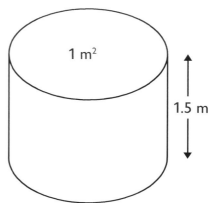

1 m²

1.5 m

(i)   Calculate the capacity, in litres, of the tank. (3)

After a heavy rainfall overnight, the tank is full of water.
Every morning, Arthur waters his plants, filling two ten-litre watering cans on each occasion.

(ii) How many days could he do this before the tank is empty? (3)

(iii) After five days:

    (a) How many litres of water has Arthur used? (1)

    (b) What is the depth of water in the tank? (3)

24. The seating capacity of Wembley Stadium in London is 90 000

At a soccer international between England and France, 90% of the seats were taken.

(i)   How many seats were taken? (2)

30% of the seats taken were occupied by supporters of France.

(ii) How many supporters of France were in the stadium? (2)

(iii) By how many did the supporters of England outnumber the supporters of France? (2)

25. *Cheery* birthday cards are made from thin card which has a mass of 160 grams per square metre.

(i)   What is the mass of a 10 cm square of the card? (2)

Each *Cheery* card is made from a simple rectangle folded in half.

There are two shapes/sizes of *Cheery* cards, as shown in the diagram below.

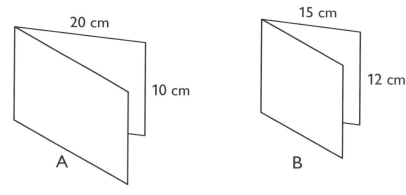

(ii) What is the area of card used to make a card of:

    (a) type A (1)

    (b) type B? (1)

(iii) What is the mass of a card of:

    (a) type A (2)

    (b) type B? (2)

26. Mary's car uses 1 litre of fuel every 7 miles when travelling at 70 miles per hour.

   (i)   How many litres of fuel will the car use on a journey of 154 miles when travelling at 70 miles per hour? (2)

   The same car uses 1 litre of fuel every 9 miles when travelling at 50 miles per hour.

   (ii) How far can the car travel on a full tank of 65 litres of fuel when travelling at 50 miles per hour? (2)

   (iii) Mary makes a journey, driving 140 miles at 70 miles per hour and then 54 miles at 50 miles per hour.

       How many litres of fuel are needed for the journey? (2)

27. Tom is building a garden shed from 7 pre-assembled pieces as shown in the diagram below.

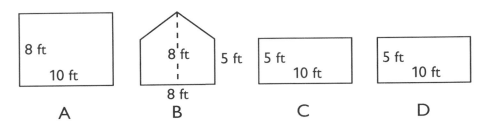

A	base	rectangle	10 ft × 8 ft	1 piece
B	end wall	pentagon	8 ft high × 8 ft	2 pieces
C	side wall	rectangle	10 ft × 5 ft	2 pieces
D	roof	rectangle	10 ft × 5 ft	2 pieces

Each piece has a 2 inch square wood frame for strength and for fixing the pieces together.

The pieces are fixed together with screws, always:

- starting in the corner
- spaced at one foot intervals.

Tom starts by fixing a piece B (end wall) to piece A (the base).

   (i)   How many screws will he use? (1)

       Hint: the answer is not 8!

Each piece must have a screw at each end.
Tom now fixes a piece C (side wall) to the base and the end wall.

   (ii) How many screws will he use to fix this piece? (2)

He now completes the structure apart from the roof.

   (iii) How many screws will he use to fix the last two walls? (3)

Tom finally fixes the two roof sheets.

   (iv) How many screws will he use to fix the two roof sheets? (2)

       Hint: don't forget that the roof sheets must be fixed to each other along the ridge.

   (v) How many screws have been used altogether? (1)

Algebra

A1 Equations and formulae

In this section the questions cover the following topics:

- Terms and expressions
- Simplification; brackets
- Substitution
- Equations
- Inequalities
- Formulae
- Modelling
- Trial and improvement

Many questions cover several topics.

In this section you should answer the questions without using a calculator except where indicated by 🖩

1. Simplify the following expressions:

    (a) $2a + a$ (1)

    (b) $2a - a$ (1)

    (c) $2a \times 2$ (1)

    (d) $2a \times a$ (1)

    (e) $2a \div 2$ (1)

2. Simplify the following expressions:

    (a) $5a + a - 4a$ (1)

    (b) $2b^2 - 5b^2 + 3b^2$ (2)

    (c) $5c^2 \times 2c$ (2)

    (d) $\dfrac{10d - 4d}{3}$ (2)

3. Simplify:

    (a) $2d + 3d + d$ (1)

    (b) $4d - 2d + 3d$ (1)

    (c) $4d \times 3d$ (2)

    (d) $\dfrac{12d}{3}$ (1)

4. (a) Simplify $11m - 2 - 7m - 2$ (2)

    (b) Factorise your answer to part (a).   (2)

5. (a) Simplify:

         (i) $3y + y + 7y$ (1)

         (ii) $3y \times y \times 7y$ (2)

         (iii) $\dfrac{10y^2}{5}$ (1)

    (b) Multiply out the brackets and simplify $3(2p - q) + 2q$ (3)

    (c) Factorise completely $12a + 18b$ (2)

6. (a) Simplify the following expressions:

         (i) $3p + 4p$ (1)

         (ii) $3p \times 4p$ (2)

         (iii) $3p - 4p + 2p$ (2)

    (b) Factorise completely $9p - 6$ (2)

7. Simplify:

    (a) $5a + 8a$ (1)

    (b) $5a - 8a$ (2)

    (c) $5a \times 8a$ (2)

    (d) $\dfrac{8a}{2}$ (2)

    (e) $(5a)^2$ (2)

8. (a) Multiply out the brackets and simplify $3(2a + c) - 4(a - 5c)$ (3)

    (b) Factorise completely $5p^2 - 10pq$ (2)

9. Simplify:

    (a) $3a + 4b + 3b$ (1)

    (b) $a \times 2b \times 3a$ (1)

    (c) $c - 5c + 3c$ (2)

    (d) $\dfrac{3d + d}{2}$ (2)

    (e) $2e^3 \times 3e^2$ (2)

    (f) $\dfrac{18e^3}{3e}$ (2)

10. Simplify:

(a) $2x^2 + 3x^3 + 3x^2 - 4x^3$ (2)

(b) $(6x)^2 - 6x^2$ (2)

(c) $\dfrac{4x + 8x}{6x}$ (2)

11. (a) Simplify:

(i) $2x^3 + 3x^3$ (1)

(ii) $2x^3 \times 3x^3$ (2)

(iii) $4x^3 \div 2xy^3$ (2)

(b) Factorise completely:

(i) $2s^2 + 2s$ (2)

(ii) $4r^2 - 6rs$ (2)

12. (a) Multiply out the brackets and simplify $2(4x - 3y) - 5(x - y)$ (3)

(b) Simplify:

(i) $(3a)^2 - 3a^2$ (2)

(ii) $\dfrac{4b^2 + 2b^2}{6b}$ (2)

(c) Factorise completely $5a^3 - 5a^2$ (2)

13. (a) Multiply out the brackets and simplify $5(1 + 2a) - 2(2a - 4)$ (3)

(b) Factorise:

(i) $4a + 14$ (1)

(ii) $6\pi r + \pi r^2$ (3)

14. (a) Simplify, by collecting like terms, $18p - 4q - 13p + 6q$ (2)

(b) Simplify the following expressions:

(i) $4pq \times pq^2$ (2)

(ii) $\dfrac{15p^3q}{10pq^2}$ (3)

15. Simplify:

(a) $\dfrac{6(x - 4)}{8x}$ (2)

(b) $5\dfrac{x^2y}{x} - 3\dfrac{xy^2}{y}$ (2)

A1

45

16. If $p = 1, q = {}^-3 , r = 5$, evaluate:

  (i) $3r + 2p - 4$ (2)

  (ii) $4p - 2q$ (2)

  (iii) $2q^2 - 5r$ (2)

17. If $x = 2, y = 3$ and $z = {}^-1$, find the value of each of the following expressions:

  (i) $3y - 4z$ (2)

  (ii) $y^2 - 5z^2$ (2)

  (iii) $\dfrac{xy}{z}$ (2)

18. If $x = 4, y = {}^-2$ and $z = {}^-3$, find the value of:

  (i) $2x - 4y$ (2)

  (ii) $x + 2y - 5z$ (2)

  (iii) $2xy^2z$ (3)

19. If $a = {}^-2, b = 1$ and $c = {}^-1$, find the value of each of the following expressions:

  (i) $3ab - 5c$ (2)

  (ii) $ac^2 - 2a^2$ (2)

  (iii) $3a(b - c)$ (2)

20. If $p = 3, q = 2$ and $r = {}^-3$, find the value of:

  (i) $5p - 6q$ (2)

  (ii) $r^2 - p^2$ (2)

  (iii) $pr - qr$ (2)

  (iv) $q(4r + 2p)$ (3)

21. If $p = 6, q = 0$ and $r = 1.5$, find the value of:

  (i) pqr (1)

  (ii) $\dfrac{2p}{r}$ (2)

  (iii) $p(q - 2r)$ (2)

22. (a) When $a = 3.3, b = 1.7$ and $c = {}^-0.8$, find the value of:

  (i) $\dfrac{a - b}{b - c}$ (2)

  (ii) $b - c^2$ (3)

(b) The formula for the area of a kite is $A = \frac{1}{2}de$

where d and e are the diagonals of the kite.

Find the value of A when $d = 3.5$ and $e = 2.4$ (3)

■■□ 23. (a) Given that $x = 2$, $y = 0.4$ and $z = {}^-0.3$, find the value of:

(i) $xz + y$ (2)

(ii) $xyz - 2$ (2)

(b) The formula for the volume, V, of a cylinder of radius r and height h is $V = \pi r^2 h$.

Taking the value of π to be $\frac{22}{7}$ calculate the volume of a metal rod of radius 0.7 cm and length 30 cm. (3)

24. William is four times as old as his son Tony. Tony is t years old.

(i) Write down, in terms of t, the age of William

(a) now (1)

(b) in 4 years' time. (1)

In 4 years' time, William will be 44 years old.

(ii) Write down an equation to express this information. (2)

(iii) Solve the equation in part (ii) to find the value of t. (2)

(iv) How many years older than Tony is William now? (2)

A1

25. In a game of numbers, Aidan chooses a number n.

Bella chooses a number which is four less than Aidan's number.

(i) Write down an expression, in terms of n, for Bella's number (1)

Chris chooses a number which is five times Aidan's number.

(ii) Write down an expression, in terms of n, for:

(a) Chris's number (1)

(b) the sum of the three numbers. Simplify your answer. (2)

The sum of the three numbers is ten.

(iii) Form an equation and solve it to find the number which Aidan chose. (2)

26. In triangle *PQR*, angle *P* is x.

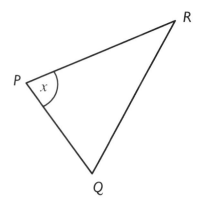

Angle *Q* is half the size of angle *P*.

(i) Write down, in terms of x, the size of angle *Q*. (1)

Angle *R* is 30 degrees larger than angle *Q*.

(ii) Write down, in terms of x, the size of angle *R*. (1)

(iii) Write down, in terms of x, an expression for the sum of angles *P*, *Q* and *R*. Simplify your answer. (2)

(iv) Write down an equation and solve it to find the value of x. (2)

(v) Write down the size of:

  (a) angle *Q* (1)

  (b) angle *R*. (1)

27. Terry buys c *Chocobars* costing n pence each.

(i) Write down an expression for the total cost of the *Chocobars* which Terry buys. (1)

Terry gives two *Chocobars* to her sister and eats three *Chocobars* herself. She finds that she now has only d *Chocobars* left.

(ii) (a) Form an equation connecting c and d. (2)

  (b) If $d = 9$, use your equation in part (ii)(a) to find the value of c. (2)

When Terry's sister bought seven *Chocobars* of the same type from the same shop, she paid £2.73 altogether.

(iii) Find the value of n. (2)

(iv) How much did Terry spend when she bought her *Chocobars*? (1)

28. r is an integer.

(i) Write down, in terms of r, the integer which is:

  (a) three more than r (1)

  (b) four times r. (1)

48

(ii) Calculate, in terms of r:

    (a) the sum of the three integers   (2)

    (b) the mean of the three integers.   (2)

(iii) If the mean is 11, form an equation in r and solve it.   (3)

(iv) Use your answer to part (iii) to write down the three integers.   (1)

29. April has found 24 snails and May has found 36 snails.

(i) Write down the ratio, in its lowest terms, of the number of snails April has to the number of snails May has.   (2)

They put some of their snails back where they found them.

Now, April has x snails and May has twice as many as April.

(ii) How many snails, in terms of x,

    (a) does May have now   (1)

    (b) do they have altogether?   (1)

(iii) What fraction of the total number of snails does May now have?   (2)

The total number of snails they now have is $\frac{7}{10}$ of the total number they started with.

(iv) Find:

    (a) the total number of snails they now have   (2)

    (b) the number of snails that April now has.   (2)

30. Solve the following equations:

(a) $w - 4 = 5$ (1)

(b) $2x = 8$ (1)

(c) $\frac{1}{2}y = 4$ (2)

(d) $2z + 2 = 8$ (2)

31. Solve the following equations:

(a) $2 + a = 7$ (1)

(b) $\frac{1}{4}b = 12$ (2)

(c) $3c - 4 = c + 2$ (2)

(d) $4(d - 2) = 16$ (3)

A1

32. Solve the following equations:

   (a) $w - 5 = 10$ (1)

   (b) $3x + 11 = 32$ (2)

   (c) $\frac{3}{4}y = 6$ (2)

   (d) $7z + 1 = z - 11$ (3)

■■□ 33. Solve the following equations:

   (a) $v - 11 = {}^-8$ (1)

   (b) $\frac{3}{7}w = 21$ (2)

   (c) $3x - 9 = 2x + 1$ (2)

   (d) $6 = \frac{y}{3} + 12$ (3)

■■□ 34. Solve these equations:

   (a) $x + 3 = {}^-3$ (2)

   (b) $4y + 5 = 17$ (2)

   (c) $z + 7 = 5z - 13$ (3)

■■□ 35. Solve these equations:

   (a) $x - 9 = 1$ (1)

   (b) $2y + 5 = 13$ (2)

   (c) $5z - 7 = 3z + 7$ (2)

■■□ 36. Solve the equation $5(z - 2) - 2(z + 4) = 24$ (4)

■■□ 37. Solve:

   (a) $p - 3 = {}^-4$ (1)

   (b) $2q + 5 = 12$ (2)

   (c) $\frac{4}{5}r = 16$ (2)

   (d) $4 - 2s = {}^-2$ (3)

■■□ 38. Solve the following equations:

   (a) $2x - 9 = 13$ (2)

   (b) $5 - y = {}^-5$ (2)

   (c) $3z + 11 = 10 - z$ (2)

■■■ 39. Solve:

    (a) $a - 6 = 19 - 4a$ (2)

    (b) $3(b + 5) = 57 - b$ (2)

    (c) $\frac{1}{2}(3c - 7) = 13$ (3)

■■■ 40. (a) Solve the equations:

        (i) $\frac{2}{3}x - 7 = 5$ (2)

        (ii) $3(y - 5) = 8y$ (3)

        (iii) $2(z + 5) - 4(z - 5) = {}^{-}4$ (3)

    (b) Solve the inequalities:

        (i) $2a + 3 > 7$ (2)

        (ii) $13 - \frac{3}{4}b > 5$ (3)

■■■ 41. (a) (i) Solve the inequality $2x - 4 \le 12$ (2)

        (ii) Write down all the positive integers which satisfy the inequality in part (a)(i).   (2)

    (b) (i) Solve the inequality $\frac{5x}{2} > 10$ (2)

        (ii) Write down the numbers in your answer to part (a)(ii) which also satisfy the inequality in part (b)(i).   (2)

A1

■■■ 42. (i) Solve the inequality $5x + 1 > {}^{-}14$ (2)

    (ii) List the negative integers which satisfy the solution to part (i).   (2)

■■■ 43. (a) Solve the equation $2(x + 5) = 7x$ (2)

    (b) (i) Solve the inequality $\frac{3}{4}p < 5$ (2)

        (ii) List the positive whole numbers which satisfy the inequality in (b)(i).   (1)

■■■ 44. (i) Solve the inequalities:

        (a) $3(2x - 1) < 15$ (2)

        (b) $\frac{1}{2}x + 3 \le x + 4$ (3)

    (ii) Write down the integers which satisfy both of the inequalities in part (i).   (1)

■■■ 45. (a) Simplify:

        (i) $(2a)^2 - 2a^2$ (2)

        (ii) $\dfrac{9a - 3a}{6a}$ (2)

    (b) Factorise $8a^2 + 12a$ (2)

    (c) Remove the brackets and simplify $4(3a - 5b) - 3(a + 2b)$ (2)

(d) (i) Solve the inequality $5a - 2 < 14$ (2)

(ii) Write down the positive whole numbers which satisfy the inequality in part (d)(i). (1)

■ ■ ■ 46. (a) Solve the equations:

(i) $\frac{1}{5}(x - 3) = 5$ (2)

(ii) $\frac{1}{7}(3w - 2) = 2$ (2)

(b) Multiply out the brackets and simplify $4(x^2 - 3) - 5(x - 6)$ (4)

(c) (i) Solve the inequality $\frac{1}{2}(x - 2\frac{1}{2}) > 1$ (3)

(ii) Solve the inequality $5 \geq \frac{3}{4}x - 4$ (3)

(iii) Draw a number line to represent the range of values of x which satisfy both inequalities. (2)

■ ■ ■ 47. Showing all your working, solve, by trial and improvement, the equation $x(x + 11) = 100$, giving your answer to two decimal places.

Copy and complete the table below, adding more lines as necessary. A start has been made for you. (4)

x	$x + 11$	$x(x + 11)$
5	16	80

■ ■ ■ 48. For the function $y = x^2 + 5x$ find, by trial and improvement, the positive value of x when y is 10
Give your answer to 3 significant figures. (5)

■ ■ ■ 49. By trial and improvement, or otherwise, find two solutions of the equation $x^2 - 10x = {}^-21$ (5)

■ ■ ■ 50. A rectangle of width w is 5.3 cm longer than it is wide.

(i) Write an expression for:

(a) the length of the rectangle (1)

(b) the area of the rectangle. (2)

The rectangle has area 43.8 cm².

(ii) Find, showing clearly how you do this,

(a) the length of the rectangle (4)

(b) the perimeter of the rectangle. (3)

■■■ 51. Bill has thought of a number which he calls b.

Sheila has thought of a number which is larger than Bill's number.

The product of their numbers is 48

(i) Write an expression in terms of b for

    (a) Sheila's number   (2)

    (b) the difference between their numbers.   (3)

The sum of the two numbers is 22.4

(ii) Find, showing clearly how you do this,

    (a) Bill's number   (2)

    (b) Sheila's number   (1)

    (c) the difference between the two numbers.   (1)

■■■ 52. The length of the rectangle below is 4 cm more than its width, x.

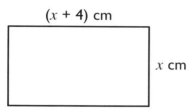

(x + 4) cm

x cm

(i) Write an expression, in terms of x, for the length of the rectangle.   (1)

(ii) Show that the area of the rectangle, in terms of x, is $x^2 + 4x$ (2)

The area of the rectangle is 50 cm².

(iii) Find, by trial and improvement, the value of x correct to 2 decimal places.

(Copy the table below and extend the number of lines of working, as necessary.)   (5)

x	x^2	$4x$	$x^2 + 4x$

■■■ 53. (a) A cube, with edges x cm long, has a total surface area of 37.5 cm².

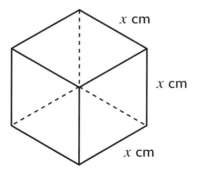

x cm

x cm

x cm

Calculate the value of x.   (3)

(b) A cuboid is x cm long, $(x - 2)$ cm wide and 4 cm high.

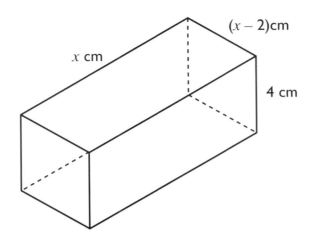

$(x - 2)$cm

x cm

4 cm

(i) Show that the total surface area of the cuboid can be represented by the expression $2x^2 + 12x - 16$ (4)

The total surface area is 94 cm².

(ii) Show that $2x^2 + 12x - 110 = 0$ (1)

(iii) By 'trial and improvement' find the value of x. (3)

Copy and complete the table below, adding more lines as necessary.

x	x^2	$2x^2$	$12x$	$2x^2 + 12x - 110$

■ ■ ■ 54. (i) Solve the following inequalities:

(a) $4 + 3x < 29$ (2)

(b) $\frac{1}{2}x - 1 \geq {}^-4$ (2)

(ii) List the integers which satisfy both inequalities. (3)

■ ■ ■ 55. (i) Factorise the expression $5x^2 + 2x$ (2)

(ii) By trial and improvement, find two possible solutions (one positive and one negative) for the equation $5x^2 + 2x - 16 = 0$

Show all your working clearly. (8)

■ ■ ■ 56. (a) Factorise $4x^2 + 2x$ (2)

(b) (i) Simplify the equation $2x^2 + 7x = {}^-4$ into the form $ax(x + b) = {}^-4$ (2)

(ii) By trial and improvement, find a value of x to 2 decimal places. (6)

A2 Sequences and functions

In this section the questions cover the following topics:
- Sequences
- Linear functions and their graphs
- Quadratic functions and their graphs
- Simultaneous equations

Many questions cover several topics.

In this section questions should be answered without using a calculator.

1. Write down the next two terms in each of the following sequences:

    (a) 53, 47, 41, 35, … (2)

    (b) 1, 5, 9, 13, 17, … (2)

    (c) 256, 128, 64, 32, … (2)

2. (a) For the sequence 4, 8, 12, 16, 20, … find:

    (i) the 6th term (1)

    (ii) the 8th term. (1)

    (b) For the sequence 4, 7, 10, 13, 16, … find:

    (i) the 6th term (1)

    (ii) the 8th term. (1)

    (c) For the sequence 1, 1, 2, 3, 5, 8, … find:

    (i) the 8th term (2)

    (ii) the 12th term. (2)

3. Write down the next two terms in each of the following sequences:

    (a) 2, 9, 16, 23, …. (2)

    (b) 1, 3, 9, 27, …. (2)

    (c) 71, 35, 17, 8, …. (4)

4. (a) When we apply the rule '**multiply by 5 and then subtract 4**' to the sequence beginning with 2, we get

    2, 6, 26, ….

    Write down the next three terms of the sequence. (3)

    (b) Apply the rule '**subtract 2 and then multiply by 3**' to write down the second, third, fourth and fifth terms of the sequence beginning with 4 (4)

55

5. Find the next two terms in each of the following sequences:

(a) $\frac{10}{11}$, $\frac{9}{10}$, $\frac{8}{9}$, $\frac{7}{8}$, ... (2)

(b) 107, 89, 71, 53, ... (2)

(c) 8991, 2997, 999, 333, ... (2)

6. (a) Write down the next two terms in each of the following sequences:

(i) 2, 5, 9, 14, 20, ... (2)

(ii) 4, 16, 36, 64, ... (2)

(iii) 1, 4, 5, 9, 14, ... (2)

(b) For the sequence 1, 4, 7, 10, 13, ... write down:

(i) the 6th term (1)

(ii) the 10th term (1)

(iii) the nth term (2)

(iv) the 100th term of the sequence. (2)

7. For the sequence 5, 8, 11, 14, ...

(i) write down the next two terms (1)

(ii) write down the formula for the nth term (2)

(iii) calculate the 20th term (1)

(iv) find the value of n when the nth term equals 125 (2)

(v) calculate the first term which is greater than 1000 (2)

8. (i) For the sequence: $t_n = n^2 - 5$, write down:

(a) the first term (t_1) (1)

(b) the 100th term (t_{100}). (1)

(ii) Find the smallest value of n for which $t_n > 500$ (2)

9. (i) For the sequence $t_n = \dfrac{2n - 1}{6n + 1}$, write down:

(a) the first term (1)

(b) the 100th term. (1)

(ii) What happens to t_n as n gets very large? (2)

■■■ 10. Consider the sequence whose nth term T_n is given by $T_n = \dfrac{n^2}{4}$

$\frac{1}{4}, 1, 2\frac{1}{4}, 4, \ldots$

(i)   Show that the 10th term of this sequence, T_{10}, is 25   (2)

The difference between the consecutive terms in the above sequence forms another sequence:

$\frac{3}{4}, 1\frac{1}{4}, 1\frac{3}{4}, 2\frac{1}{4}, \ldots$

i.e. $1 - \frac{1}{4} = \frac{3}{4}, 2\frac{1}{4} - 1 = 1\frac{1}{4}$ and so on.

The nth term of this new sequence (the first difference sequence) is given by the expression $\frac{1}{2}n + \frac{1}{4}$ or $\frac{1}{2}(n + \frac{1}{2})$

The difference between consecutive terms in the first difference sequence is constant and equals $\frac{1}{2}$

i.e. $1\frac{1}{4} - \frac{3}{4} = \frac{1}{2}, 1\frac{3}{4} - 1\frac{1}{4} = \frac{1}{2}$ and so on.

(ii)   Complete the table below for similar sequences.

T_n	sequence	1st difference sequence	nth term of 1st difference	2nd difference constant
$\frac{1}{4}n^2$	$\frac{1}{4}, 1, 2\frac{1}{4}, 4, \ldots$	$\frac{3}{4}, 1\frac{1}{4}, 1\frac{3}{4}, \ldots$	$\frac{1}{2}(n + \frac{1}{2})$	$\frac{1}{2}$
$\frac{1}{2}n^2$	$\frac{1}{2}, 2, 4\frac{1}{2}, 8, \ldots$	$1\frac{1}{2}, 2\frac{1}{2}, 3\frac{1}{2}, \ldots$	$n + \frac{1}{2}$	1
n^2				
$2n^2$				

(4)

(4)

A2

11. On a copy of the grid below, draw and label the lines with equations:

    (a) $x = 3$ (1)

    (b) $y = 5$ (1)

    (c) $x = {}^{-}4$ (1)

    (d) $y = x$ (2)

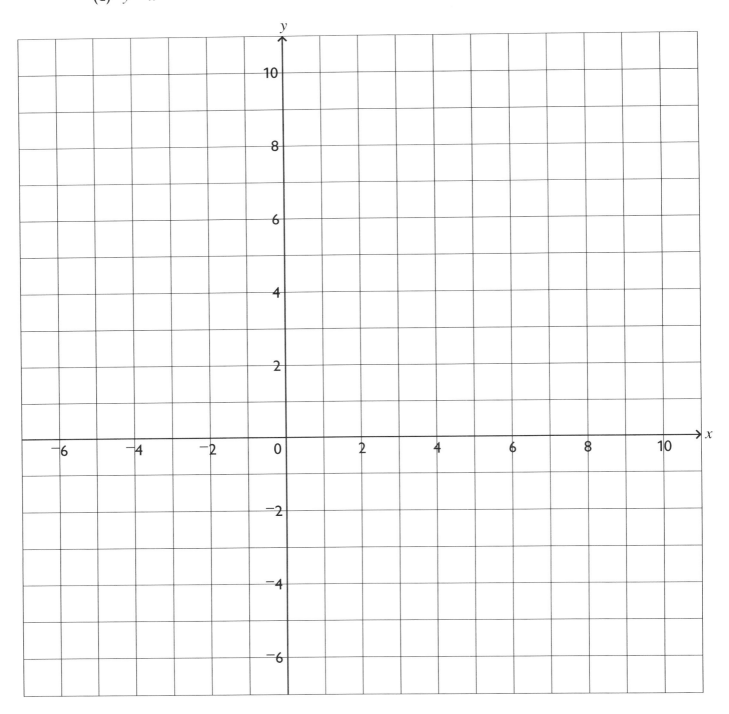

12. (i) A straight line has the equation $y = x + 3$

   (a) For this straight line, copy and complete the table of values below. (2)

x	$^-3$	0	3
y			

   (b) On a copy of the grid below, draw the graph of $y = x + 3$ (2)

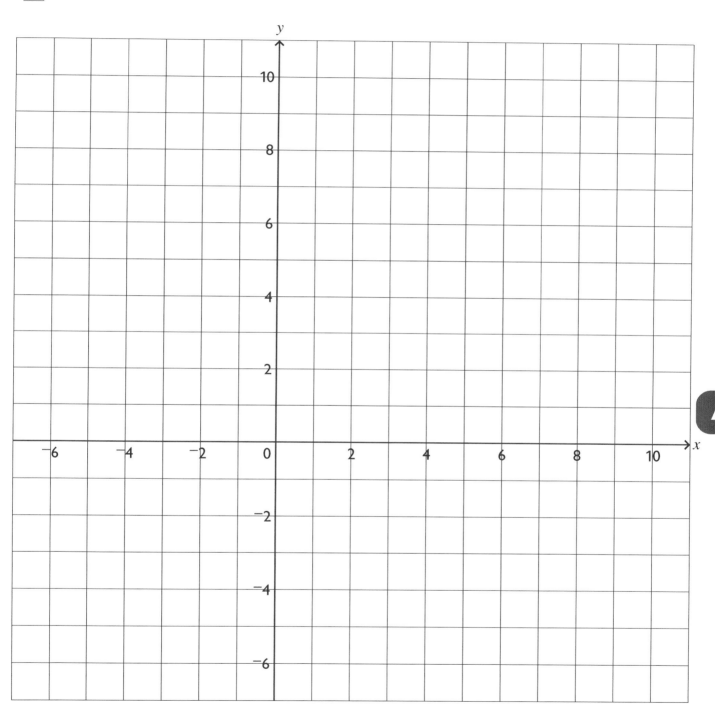

A2

(ii) Another straight line has the equation $y = 5 - x$

    (a) Copy and complete the table below.   (2)

x	⁻3	0	3
y			

    (b) On your grid, draw the graph of $y = 5 - x$ (1)

(iii) Write down the co-ordinates of the point of intersection of the two straight lines.   (2)

13. (i) Copy and complete the table for each of the following functions:

    (a) $y = x + 1$ (2)

x	⁻2	1	4
y			

    (b) $y = 7 - x$ (2)

x	⁻2	1	4
y			

(ii) On a copy of the grid below, draw the graph of:

   (a) $y = x + 1$ (1)

   (b) $y = 7 - x$ (2)

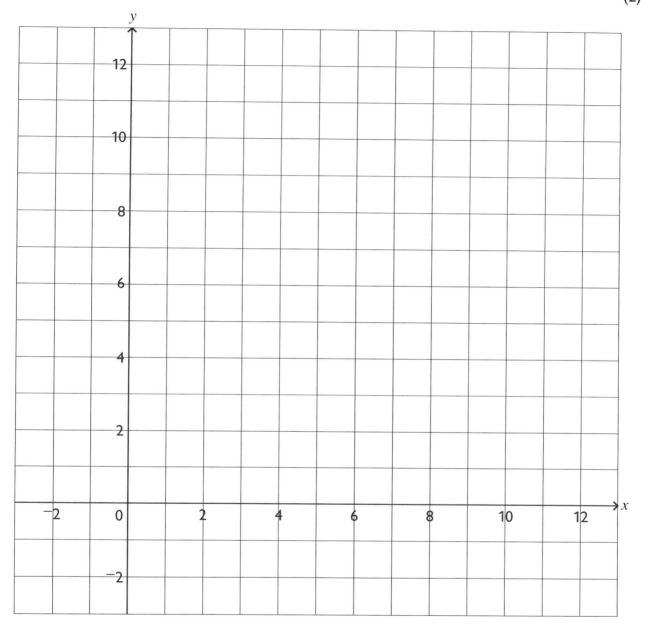

A2

(iii) On the same grid, draw and label the line $y = 1$ (1)

(iv) Circle the points, with whole number co-ordinates, which lie within the triangle enclosed by the three lines.   (2)

14. On the grid below the equation of the line A is $y = 3 - x$

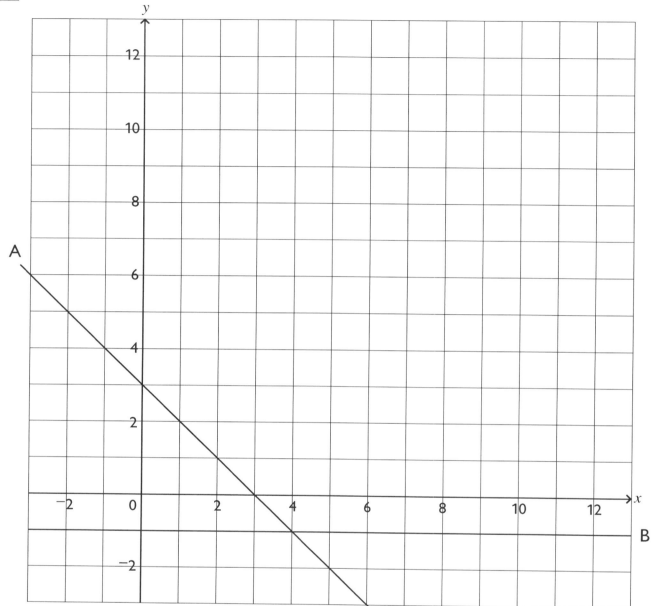

(i) Write down the co-ordinates of two points which lie on the line A. (2)

(ii) Write down the equation of line B. (1)

(iii) (a) Copy and complete the following mapping table for the line C. (2)

x	−1	0	1	2	x
y	1	3	5		

(b) Hence write down the equation of line C. (1)

(c) Copy the diagram and draw the line C. (2)

(iv) Find the area of the shaded region bounded by the three lines A, B and C. (3)

■ ■ ■ 15. (i) Copy and complete this table of values for the function $y = x^2$ (2)

x	$^{-}3$	$^{-}2$	$^{-}1$	0	1	2	3
y		4			1		9

(ii) On a copy of the grid below, draw the graph of $y = x^2$ (2)

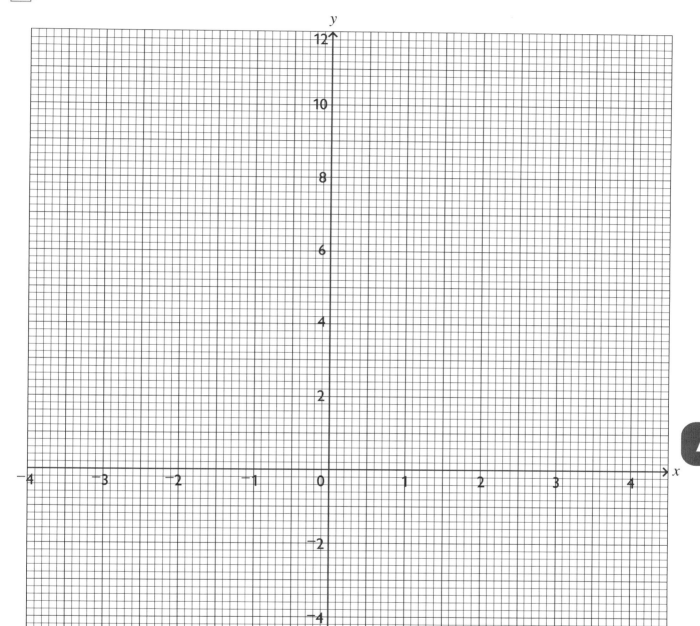

A2

(iii) On the same grid draw the line $y = 7$ (1)

(iv) Estimate the x co-ordinate of the point in the first quadrant where the graph meets the line. (1)

■ ■ ■ 16. (i) Copy and complete the table of values for the function $y = x^2 - 2$ (2)

x	$^-3$	$^-2$	$^-1$	0	1	2	3
y	7				$^-1$		

(ii) On a copy of the grid below, draw the graph of $y = x^2 - 2$ (2)

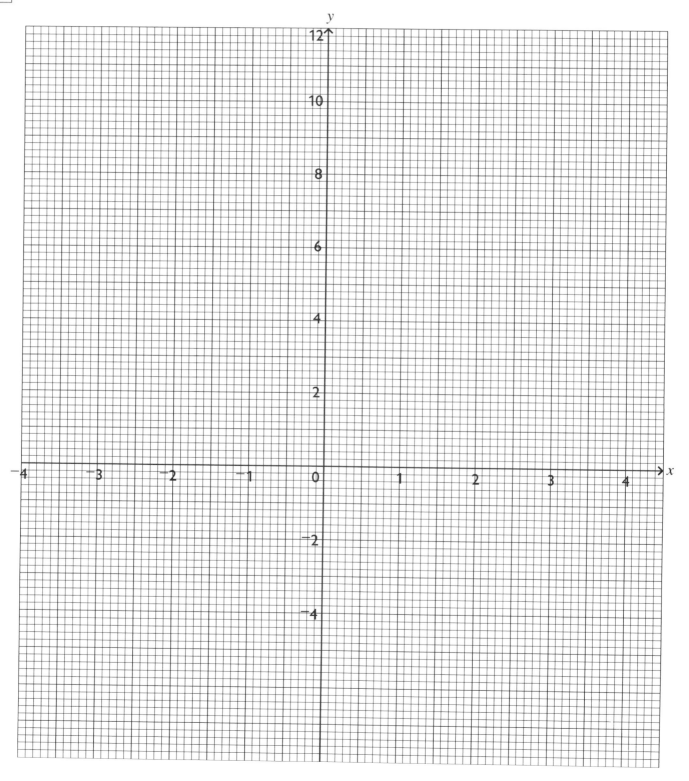

(iii) On the same grid, plot the graph of $y = x$ (2)

(iv) Write down the co-ordinates of the points where the graphs intersect. (2)

■■■ 17. (i) Copy and complete the table below for $y = \frac{1}{2}x^2 - 3$ (3)

x	$^-3$	$^-2$	$^-1$	0	1	2	3	4
$\frac{1}{2}x^2$					0.5		4.5	
y					$^-2.5$			

A2

(ii) On a copy of the grid below, draw the graph of $y = \frac{1}{2}x^2 - 3$ (2)

(iii) By taking suitable values for x and y, or otherwise, draw the graph of
$y = x - 1$ on the same grid. (3)

(iv) Circle each point with integer co-ordinates which lies entirely inside the region
bounded by $y = \frac{1}{2}x^2 - 3$ and $y = x - 1$ (1)

(v) Which point, circled in part (iv), has co-ordinates (x, y) where the value of
$x - y$ is largest? (1)

■■■ 18. (i) By substituting values for x into the equation $y = x^2 - 2x$, complete a
copy of this table of values for y. (3)

x	$^-2$	$^-1$	$-\frac{1}{2}$	0	$\frac{1}{2}$	1	$1\frac{1}{2}$	2	3	4
y					$-\frac{3}{4}$					

A2

6 (ii) On a copy of the grid below, draw the graph of $y = x^2 - 2x$ (2)

(iii) Substitute values for x into the equation $y = x + 3$ (2)

x	$^-3$	0	3
y			

(iv) On the same grid, draw the graph of $y = x + 3$ (1)

(v) Write down the co-ordinates of the point of intersection of the two graphs in the first quadrant. (2)

■■■ 19. (i) Copy and complete the table of values for the function:

(a) $y = x^2$ (2)

x	$^-2$	$^-1$	0	1	2
y		1			

(b) $y = 3 - x^2$ (2)

x	$^-2$	$^-1$	0	1	2
y			3		

A2

69

(ii) On a copy of the grid below, draw the two graphs of $y = x^2$ and $y = 3 - x^2$ (4)

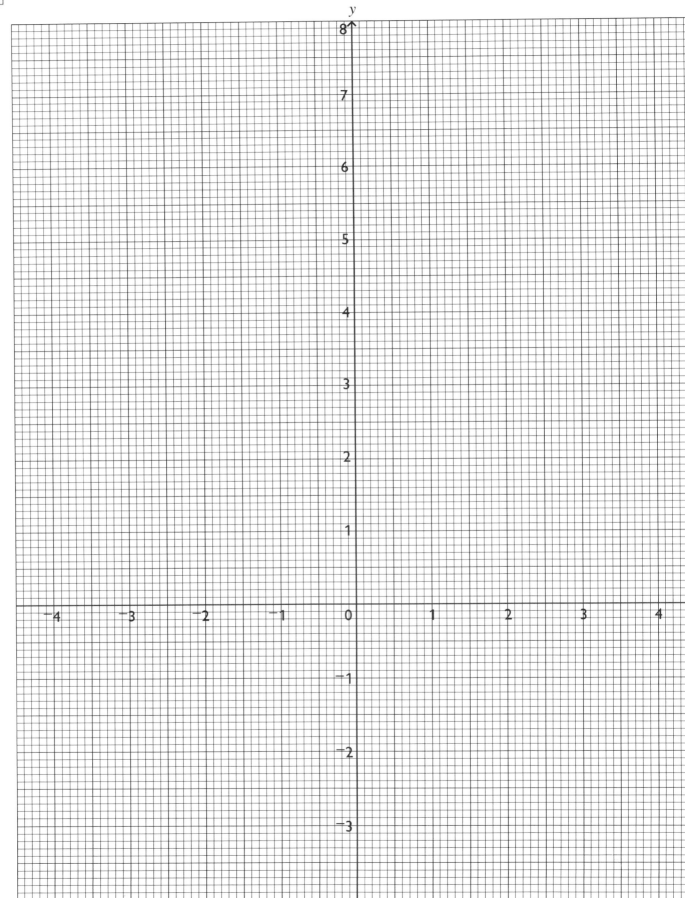

(iii) Estimate the co-ordinates of the two points of intersection of the two graphs. (4)

■■■ 20. John has a two-stage function machine.

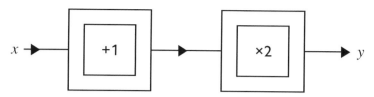

(i) Copy and complete this table of input and output values. (3)

input (x)	output (y)
⁻1	
2	
4	

(ii) On a copy of the grid below, draw and label a graph of the function represented by John's machine. (3)

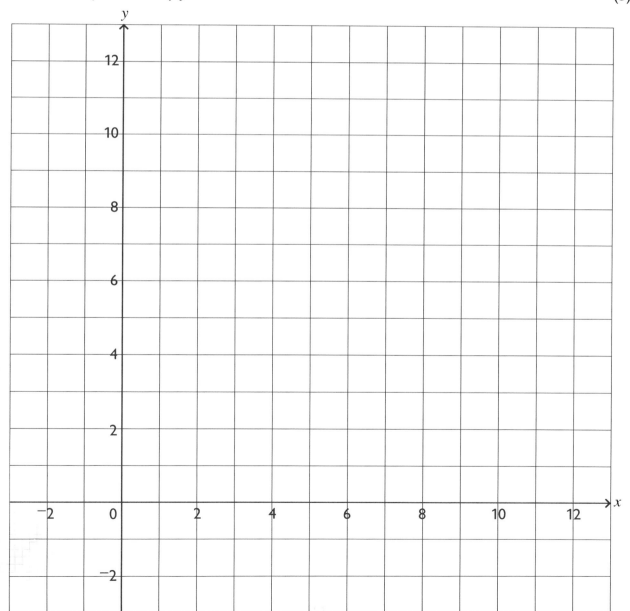

■ ■ ■ 21. Morag has a two-stage function machine which represents a quadratic function.

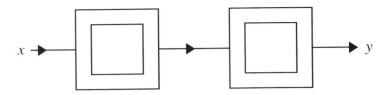

Unfortunately the labels have fallen off the function machine.

Morag can find five labels.

| add 3 | | square | | subtract 3 | | add 1 | | multiply by 3 |

Fortunately, Morag has a printout of some input (x) and output (y) values for her machine.

input (x)	output (y)
$^-1$	16
2	1
5	4

   (i)   Copy the drawing of Morag's machine and write in the labels.   (2)

   (ii)   For Morag's machine, which input would give an output of 100?   (2)

■ ■ ■ 22.   (i)   Copy and complete the table of values for the graph of $y = x^2 + x$ (4)

x	$^-3$	$^-2$	$^-1$	0	1	2	3
x^2		4	1	0			
y			0				

   (ii)   (a)   What is the value of x when y has its lowest value?   (1)

           (b)   What is the lowest value of y?   (1)

6 (iii) On a copy of the grid below, draw the graph of $y = x^2 + x$ (3)

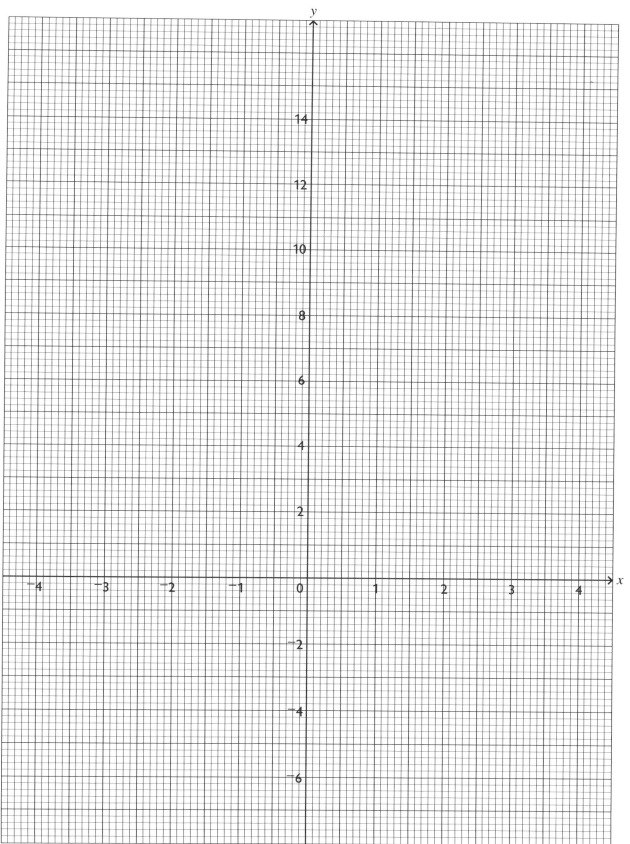

A2

(iv) Use your graph to find the values of x where the graph crosses the line $y = 3$ (2)

■■■ 23. On the grid below, several points have been plotted for the function $y = x^2 - x - 2$

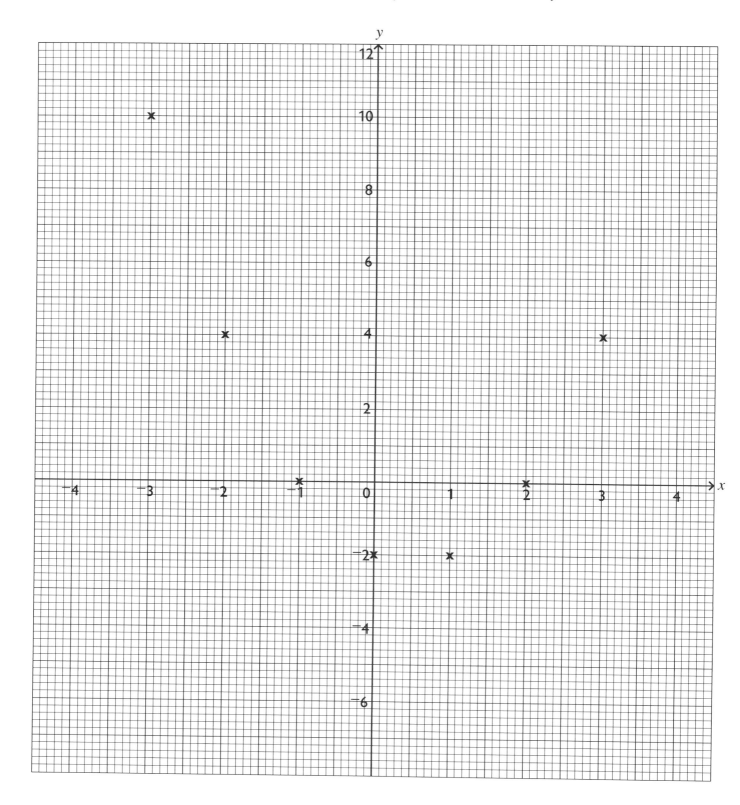

(i) What is the equation of the line of symmetry of the curve through these points? (1)

(ii) What are the co-ordinates of the lowest point on the curve? (2)

(iii) (a) Plot this point on a copy of the grid. (1)

(b) Draw the graph of the function $y = x^2 - x - 2$ (2)

■■■ 24. (i) Copy and complete the table of values for the function $y = \frac{1}{2}x^2 - \frac{1}{2}x$ (5)

x	-3	-2	-1	0	$\frac{1}{2}$	1	2	3	4
x^2	9								
$\frac{1}{2}x^2$	$4\frac{1}{2}$								
$\frac{1}{2}x$	$-1\frac{1}{2}$								
y	6								

A2

75

(ii) On a copy of the grid below, draw the graph of $y = \frac{1}{2}x^2 - \frac{1}{2}x$ (3)

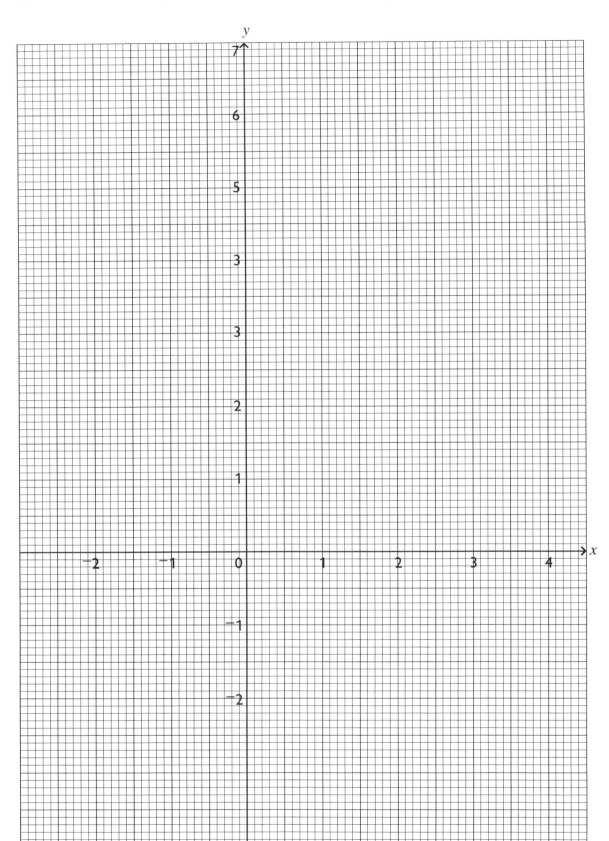

(iii) A straight line has the equation $y = 2 - x$

    (a) Copy and complete the table of values below.

x	$^-1$	0	2
y			

(2)

    (b) On the same grid, draw the graph of $y = 2 - x$ (1)

(iv) Write down the co-ordinates of the points of intersection of the two graphs. (2)

■■■ 25. (i) Copy the tables and write the output values for the functions represented by the three machines below.

    (a) Machine P: $y = x^2 - 1$ (2)

Machine P

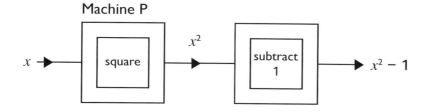

input (x)	output (y)
2	
$^-3$	

    (b) Machine Q: $y = (x - 1)^2$ (2)

Machine Q

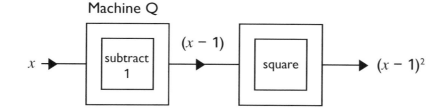

input (x)	output (y)
2	
$^-3$	

A2

(c) Machine R: $y = x^2 - 2x + 1$ (3)

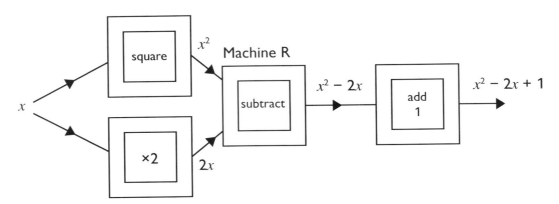

input (x)	output (y)
2	
−3	

(ii) Compare your answers to part (i). What do you notice?   (2)

■■■ 26. Mike is m years old and his older brother Nathan is n years old.

(i)   Write down expressions, in terms of m and n, for:

(a)   the sum of their ages   (1)

(b)   the difference between their ages.   (1)

They calculate that the sum of their ages is 25 years.

(ii) Write down an equation, in terms of m and n, to show this information.   (2)

Nathan is 7 years older than Mike.

(iii) Use this information and your answer to part (ii) to find Nathan's age.   (3)

■■■ 27. x and y are two integers.

$3x + 2y = 44$

$x - 2y = 4$

Solve the equations simultaneously to find the two integers.   (4)

■■■ 28. Solve the simultaneous equations:

$2a - 4b = 6$

$a + 3b = 13$ (4)

29. Sally adds two numbers and then multiplies the result by 2

She gets 22

The difference between her numbers is 1

    (i)   Write two equations to represent this information.   (3)

    (ii) Solve the two equations simultaneously to find Sally's two numbers.   (3)

30. Solve the simultaneous equations:

$$5x + 4y = {}^-2$$
$$2x - 3y = 13$$

  (5)

31. The sum of two numbers is 43 and the difference between them is 30

    (i)   Write down two equations to represent this information.   (4)

    (ii) Solve the equations simultaneously to find the two numbers.   (3)

    (iii) What is the product of the two numbers?   (2)

32. The nth term of a sequence is given as $n^2 + 2n + 6$

    (i)   Find:

        (a) the 5th term   (2)

        (b) the 6th term   (2)

    (ii) After the 5th term, which is the next term that is a prime number?   (3)

    (iii) Which is the first term of the sequence that is a square number?   (2)

33. Rory has x pound coins and y fifty pence coins. Clare has x fifty pence coins and y pound coins.

Rory has £8.50 and Clare has one pound more than Rory.

    (i)   Write equations to represent the coins owned by:

        (a) Rory   (2)

        (b) Clare   (2)

    (ii) Solve the equations simultaneously to find the values of:

        (a) x (2)

        (b) y (2)

A2

34. (a) Showing all your working, solve the following two equations simultaneously.   (5)

$$12x + 7 = 5y$$
$$5x = y - \frac{3}{4}$$

    (b) The sum of two numbers is 60 and the difference between them is 26

        What is:

        (i)   the smaller of the two numbers   (3)

        (ii) the product of the two numbers.   (2)

Shape, space and measures

S1 Measures

In this section the questions cover the following topics:

- Metric units and Imperial units
- Constructions
- Areas and volumes
- Circles
- Speed

Many questions cover several topics.

In this section, questions should be answered without using a calculator.

1. Convert each of the following measurements into the units shown:

    (a) 3.5 metres into centimetres   (1)

    (b) 736 millimetres into centimetres   (1)

    (c) 4.05 litres into millilitres   (1)

    (d) 690 grams into kilograms.   (1)

2. One night, the temperature in my shed dropped from 7.6 °C to ⁻4.8 °C.
    By how many degrees did the temperature drop?   (2)

3. (i)   Choose an estimate of the mass of an ordinary soccer ball from the following list.

          4 g   100 g   400 g   1 kg   4 kg   (2)

    (ii) Choose an estimate of the *circumference* of a soccer ball from the following list.

          20 cm   30 cm   40 cm   50 cm   70 cm   (2)

    (iii) Choose an estimate of the volume of a soccer ball from the following list.

          500 cm³   1000 cm³   2000 cm³   4000 cm³   8000 cm³   (2)

4. (i)   Construct triangle ABC with AB = 9 cm, BC = 7.5 cm and AC = 8 cm.   (4)

    (ii) Measure and write down the size of:

          (a) angle ABC (1)

          (b) angle BAC.   (1)

5. (i)   Construct triangle ABC in which AB = 11 cm, BC = 9.5 cm and angle ABC = 45°.   (3)

    (ii) Measure and write down the shortest distance from C to AB.   (1)

■■□ 6. The angles of a triangle are in the ratio 1 : 2 : 3

    (i) Calculate the angles of the triangle. (2)

    The shortest side of the triangle is 6 cm.

    (ii) Construct the triangle. (2)

    (iii) Use measurements from your diagram to calculate the area of the triangle. (2)

7. Triangle ABC is isosceles.

    AB and AC both measure 8 cm and BC measures 5 cm.

    (i) Construct triangle ABC. (2)

    (ii) Measure angle ACB. (1)

8. (i) Construct a regular hexagon ABCDEF of side 4 cm. (3)

    (ii) Measure the length of the diagonal AD. (1)

    (iii) By taking suitable measurements, estimate the area of the hexagon. (3)

9. The distance from P to Q is 12 metres.

    (i) Use a scale of 1 : 100 to make a scale drawing of the line PQ. (2)

    (ii) On your drawing, mark the point R on PQ which is twice as far from P as it is from Q. (2)

    (iii) On your drawing, represent the area which is 3 metres or less from R. (3)

10. A square has diagonals of length 8 centimetres.

    (i) Make an accurate drawing of the square. (3)

    (ii) Measure the length of a side of the square. (1)

    (iii) Calculate, giving your answers to 1 decimal place,

        (a) the perimeter of the square (2)

        (b) the area of the square. (2)

S1

11. (a) By taking suitable measurements, find:

      (i)   the area   (2)

      (ii) the perimeter of this shape.   (2)

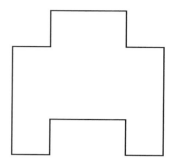

(b) By taking suitable measurements, find:

      (i)   the area   (2)

      (ii) the perimeter of this shape.   (1)

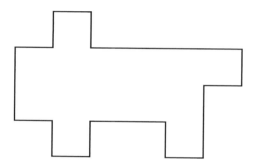

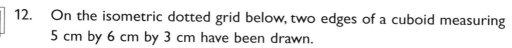

12. On the isometric dotted grid below, two edges of a cuboid measuring 5 cm by 6 cm by 3 cm have been drawn.

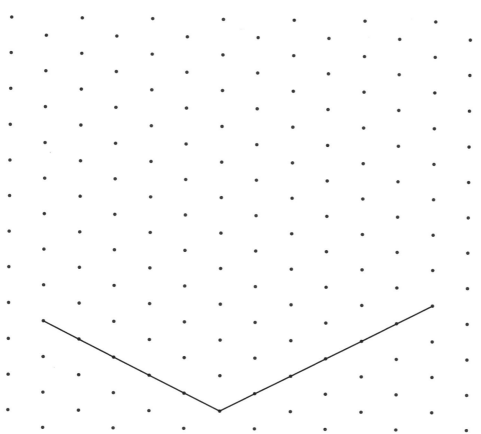

(i)   Copy and complete the drawing.   (3)

(ii) Calculate the volume of the cuboid.   (2)

(iii) Calculate the total surface area of the cuboid.   (4)

13. Joanne has made a cuboid 4.5 cm long, 4 cm wide and 2 cm high.

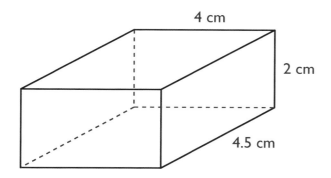

(i) What is the volume of Joanne's cuboid?   (2)

(ii) Work out the total surface area of Joanne's cuboid.   (4)

14. The diagram shows a rectangular box which just holds 6 golf balls. Each ball has diameter 43 mm. Give all of your answers to the nearest cubic centimetre.

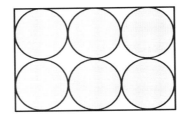

(i) Calculate, in cubic centimetres, the volume of the box when empty. (3)

The volume of a golf ball is 41.6 cm³.

(ii) Calculate the volume of:

(a) 6 golf balls (2)

(b) the empty space in the box when it contains 6 balls. (1)

15. An Ordnance Survey map has a scale of 1 : 50 000

(i) What distance (in metres) on the land is represented by 1 cm on the map? (2)

(ii) What will be the distance on the map between Dufftown and Keith if the distance on the land is 19 km? (2)

(iii) The distance on the map between two bridges is 6.5 cm. What is the distance, in kilometres, between the bridges? (2)

(iv) The measurements on the map of a rectangular field are 0.5 cm by 0.4 cm. Find, showing your working clearly, the area of the field:

(a) in square metres (3)

(b) in hectares (1 hectare = 10 000 m²). (1)

■■□ 16. A circular button has radius 6 mm.

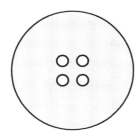

Take π to be 3 in this question.

(i) Calculate the circumference of the button. (2)

Each hole (for the thread) has an area of 2 mm².

(ii) Calculate the area of the top of the button. (3)

84

The thickness of the button is 1.5 mm.

(iii) Using your answer to part (ii), calculate the volume of the button. (2)

■■□ 17. A thin circular plastic disc has diameter 28 centimetres and mass 400 grams.

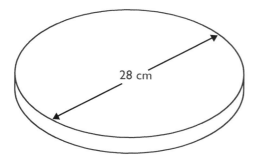

Take π to be $\frac{22}{7}$ in this question.

(i) Calculate:

    (a) the circumference of the disc (2)

    (b) the area of the disc. (3)

A circular hole of diameter 14 cm is cut from the centre of the disc to make a 'throwing ring'.

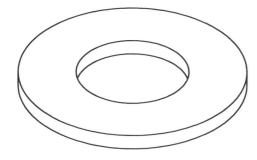

(ii) Calculate:

    (a) the area of the ring (2)

    (b) the mass of the ring. (3)

■■□ 18. Take π to be $\frac{22}{7}$ in this question.

(a) Calculate the area, in m², of a circle with radius 0.7 m. (2)

(b) Calculate the volume, in cm³, of a rectangular box with dimensions
12 cm × 6.5 cm × 5 cm (2)

S1

85

■■□ 19. The diagram shows a lawn surrounded by a path which is 1.4 m wide. The curved ends of the lawn are semicircles of diameter 14 m.

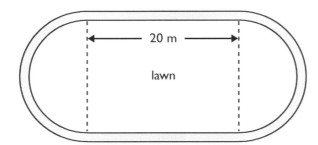

Take π to be $\frac{22}{7}$ in this question.

Calculate:

(i)   the width of the rectangular part of the lawn   (1)

(ii) the area of the rectangular part of the lawn   (1)

(iii) the area of the two semicircular parts of the lawn   (2)

(iv) the area of the rectangular parts of the path   (2)

(v)   the area, to the nearest square metre, of the curved parts of the path   (3)

(vi) using your answers to parts (iv) and (v), the total area of the path.   (1)

■■□ 20. The base of a cylindrical tin of soup has circumference 22 cm.

(i)   Taking π to be $\frac{22}{7}$, calculate:

      (a) the radius of the base of the tin   (2)

      (b) the area of the base of the tin.   (2)

The height of the tin is 11 cm.

(ii) Calculate the volume of the soup. (Assume that the tin is completely full of soup.)   (2)

Sarah pours the contents of the tin into a cylindrical pan with diameter 14 cm.

(iii) Calculate the depth of soup in the pan.   (3)

■ ■ ☐ 21. The pie chart drawn to scale below has area 72 cm².

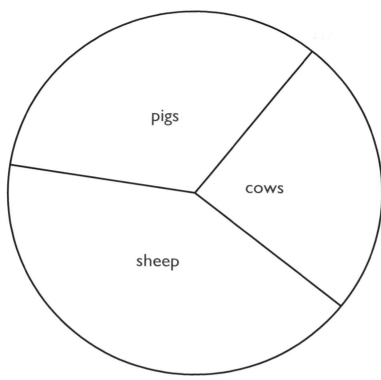

(i) Calculate:

    (a) the area representing cows   (2)

    (b) the area representing sheep.   (2)

(ii) Measure, to the nearest millimetre, the radius of the pie chart.   (1)

(iii) Taking π to be 3.14, and using your answer to part (ii), calculate, to 1 decimal place:

    (a) the circumference of the pie chart   (3)

    (b) the length of the arc of the sector representing pigs.   (2)

There are 720 animals altogether.

(iv) How many sheep are there?   (2)

■ ■ ☐ 22. Natalie runs 200 metres in 25 seconds. What is her average speed:

(i) in metres per second   (2)

(ii) in kilometres per hour?   (3)

■ ■ ■ 23. (a) What is a prism? Explain as fully as you can.   (3)

    (b) An upright cylindrical storage tank has diameter 2 metres.
        The water level is 5 metres from the bottom of the tank.
        Find, in cubic metres, the volume of water.   (4)

S1

S2 Shape

In this section the questions cover the following topics:

- Plane shapes and their properties
- Solid shapes and their properties
- Nets
- Symmetry

Many questions cover several topics.

In this section questions should be answered without using a calculator.

1. (i) Draw the grid below and plot the following points:

   $A\,(^-2, 1)$ $B\,(1, 3)$ $C\,(4, 1)$ $D\,(1, ^-1)$ (2)

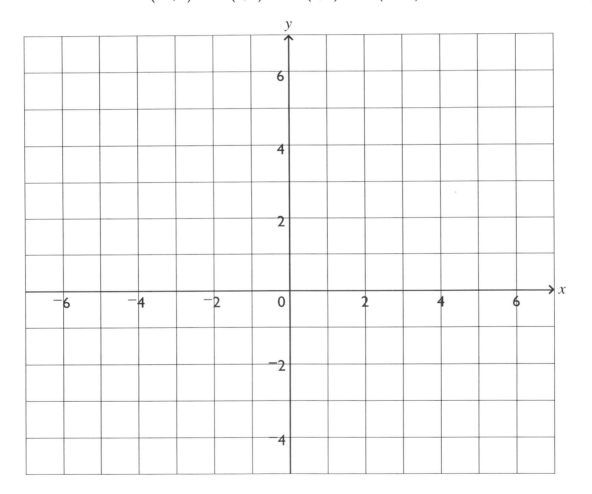

   (ii) (a) Join the points to form the shape *ABCD*.   (1)

   (b) Name the shape *ABCD*.   (1)

   (iii) (a) Draw all lines of symmetry on *ABCD*.   (1)

   (b) Name the lines you have drawn.   (1)

(iv) What is the order of symmetry of *ABCD*? (1)

(v) What is the area of *ABCD*? (2)

2. (a) (i) Draw a square with sides 4 cm. (1)

(ii) On your square draw all the lines of symmetry. (2)

(iii) What is the order of rotational symmetry of the square? (1)

(b) (i) Sketch a quadrilateral which has no rotational symmetry but has one line of symmetry. (2)

(ii) Name the quadrilateral you have drawn in part (b) (i). (1)

3. (a) A shape is described as being two-dimensional with four equal sides of length 5 cm. One of the angles is 70°.

(i) Draw the shape as accurately as you can. (4)

(ii) Name the shape you have drawn in part (i). (1)

(b) In the diagram below, *PQRS* has two pairs of equal sides.

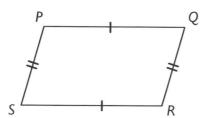

(i) Describe, as fully as you can, the symmetry of *PQRS*. (2)

(ii) Write down another fact about the sides of *PQRS*. (1)

(iii) Write down a fact about the angles of *PQRS*. (1)

◀■□ 4. *A*, *B*, *C* and *D* are four vertices of a regular polygon with interior angles of 135°.

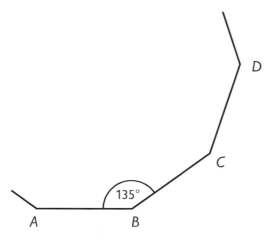

(i) Find the size of an exterior angle of the polygon. (2)

(ii) How many sides does the polygon have? (2)

(iii) Find the sum of all the interior angles of the polygon. (1)

(iv) Name the polygon. (1)

■■□ 5. (a) Calculate the interior angle of a regular decagon. (3)

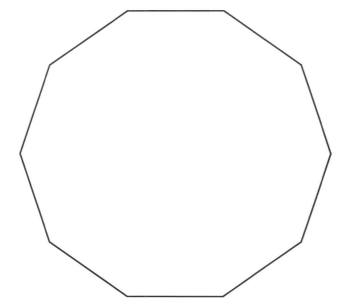

(b) *P*, *Q* and *R* are vertices of a regular polygon with exterior angles equal to 72°.

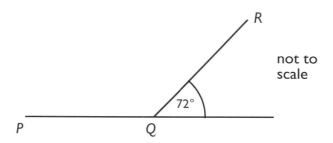

not to scale

(i) Name the polygon. (2)

(ii) What is the order of rotational symmetry of the polygon? (1)

■■□ 6. *ABCD* is part of a regular polygon with exterior angles of 40°.

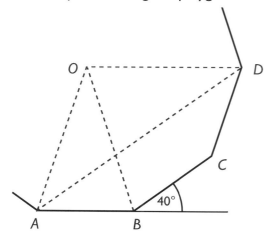

(i)   Calculate:

    (a)   the total number of sides   (1)

    (b)   the size of each interior angle   (1)

    (c)   the sum of all the interior angles of the polygon.   (1)

The point O is the centre of the polygon.

(ii) Calculate the size of:

    (a)   angle AOB (2)

    (b)   angle ADO.   (2)

7. The diagram below shows the net of a prism. The prism has two faces which are isosceles trapezia and four rectangular faces.

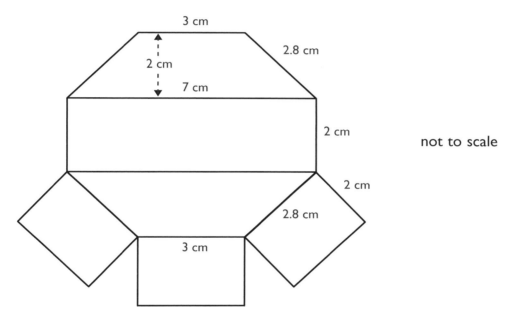

not to scale

(i)   For the completed prism, write down:

    (a)   the number of vertices   (2)

    (b)   the number of edges.   (2)

(ii) Calculate:

    (a)   the area of one of the isosceles trapezia   (2)

    (b)   the total surface area of the prism   (2)

    (c)   the volume of the prism.   (2)

S2

8.   On centimetre square dotted paper, draw accurately:

    (i)   a plane shape which has five sides and one line of symmetry.   (2)

    (ii) an isosceles right-angled triangle   (2)

    (iii) a kite with diagonals measuring 4 cm and 6 cm   (2)

    (iv) a shape with rotational symmetry order 4 but no line symmetry.   (2)

S3 Space

> In this section the questions cover the following topics:
> - Angles
> - Bearings and scale drawings
> - Transformations on a grid
> - Enlargement
> - Pythagoras' theorem
> - Trigonometry

Many questions cover several topics.

In this section questions should be answered without using a calculator.

1.   Calculate the size of the angles marked a, b and c.

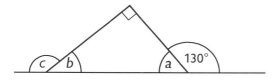

    (i)   angle a   (2)

    (ii) angle b   (2)

    (iii) angle c   (1)

2.   (a) Calculate the size of the angles marked a and b.

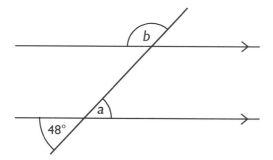

    (i)   angle *a*   (1)

    (ii) angle *b*   (2)

(b) Calculate the size of the angles marked *c* and *d*.

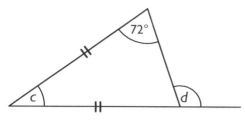

    (i)   angle *c*   (2)

    (ii) angle *d*   (2)

3.   The diagram shows three isosceles triangles. *PQR* is a straight line.

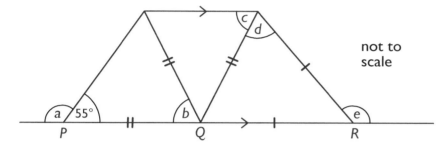

Calculate the size of:

(i)   angle *a*   (1)

(ii) angle *b*   (2)

(iii) angle *c*   (2)

(iv) angle *d*   (1)

(v) angle *e*   (2)

4.   Calculate the size of the angles marked a, b, c and d.

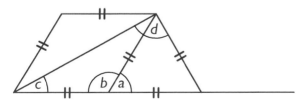

(i)   angle *a*   (1)

(ii) angle *b*   (1)

(iii) angle *c*   (2)

(iv) angle *d*   (2)

5. The diagram below shows a quadrilateral *ABCD*.

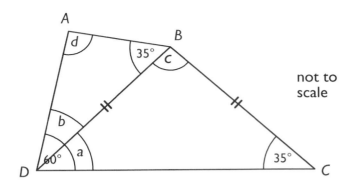

not to scale

(i) Calculate the size of:

    (a) angle *a*   (1)

    (b) angle *b*   (1)

    (c) angle *c*   (2)

    (d) angle *d*   (2)

(ii) Which type of quadrilateral is *ABCD*?   (1)

6. Find the size of the angles marked *a*, *b*, *c* and *d*.

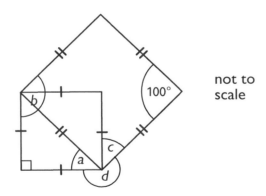

not to scale

(i) angle *a*   (1)

(ii) angle *b*   (2)

(iii) angle *c*   (2)

(iv) angle *d*   (2)

7. In the diagram below, angle *ABC* = 110° and angle *DEF* = 135°.

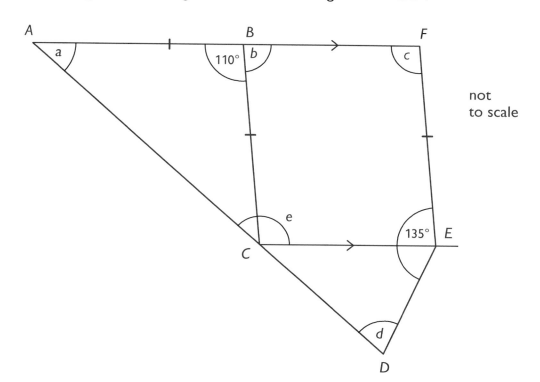

not to scale

Calculate the size of:

(i) angle *a* (1)

(ii) angle *b* (1)

(iii) angle *c* (2)

(iv) angle *d* (2)

(v) angle *e* (2)

S3

8. The diagram below is drawn to scale.

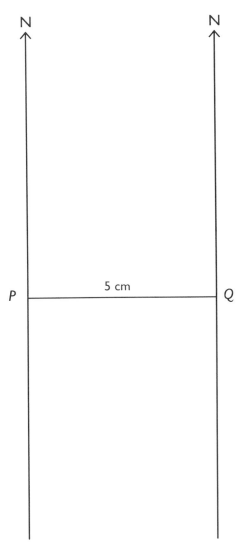

Pencilham (*P*) is 10 km west of Quackle (*Q*).

(i) What scale has been used? Give your answer:

    (a) in the form 1 cm to represent … km (1)

    (b) as a ratio 1 : … (2)

(ii) Make an accurate copy of the diagram. (2)

Rulerford is due south of Pencilham and south-west of Quackle.

(iii) On your diagram, mark the position of Rulerford. (2)

(iv) What is the distance, in kilometres:

    (a) from Pencilham to Rulerford (1)

    (b) from Rulerford to Quackle? (2)

9. On an island there is a lighthouse (*L*) which is 750 m north-east of a cave (*C*). The sketch below is **not to scale**.

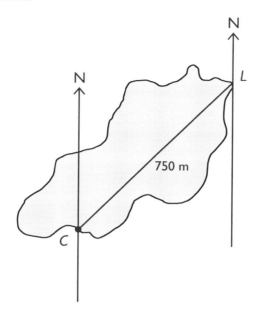

(i)   Mark a point *C* about halfway down the left-hand side, and 2 cm from the edge, of your page. Draw a north line through *C*. (1)

(ii) Using a scale of 1 : 10 000 (1 cm to represent 100 m), plot the position of the lighthouse (*L*). **You do not need to draw the island!** (2)

A fishing boat (*F*) is due east of the cave and south-east of the lighthouse.

(iii) Plot the position of the fishing boat. (2)

(iv) From your scale drawing, find how far the fishing boat is from the cave. (2)

10. Tom has given instructions to Annie. Annie is standing at a point *S*, 5 paces west of Tom (*T*).

The instructions are:

> *Take*
>
> *(a)   6 paces north*
>
> *(b)   7 paces north-west*
>
> *(c)   13 paces south*
>
> *(d)   3 paces east, then stop.*

(i)   Mark a point *S* in the centre of your page. Using a scale of 1 cm to represent 1 pace, draw an accurate scale diagram to show Annie's route. (4)

(ii) When Annie stops:

      (a) how many paces (to the nearest pace) is she from Tom (2)

      (b) in what direction would she walk to get back to *S*? (2)

S3

■■□ 11. The diagram below is to scale.

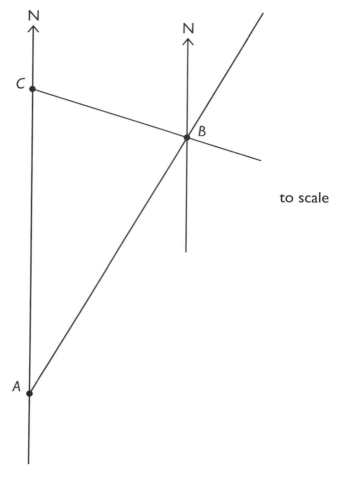

to scale

Measure carefully and write down:

(i)   the bearing of B from A   (1)

(ii) the bearing of B from C   (2)

(iii) the bearing of A from B.   (2)

■■□ 12. The diagram below is **not to scale**.

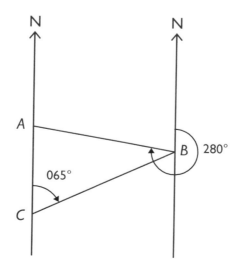

Calculate:

(i)   the bearing of *B* from *A* (2)

(ii) the bearing of *C* from *B*. (3)

■■□ 13. A windsurfer in distress can be seen from a harbour wall (*H*) and a lookout tower (*L*).
The position of the windsurfer from the harbour wall is on a bearing of 120°.

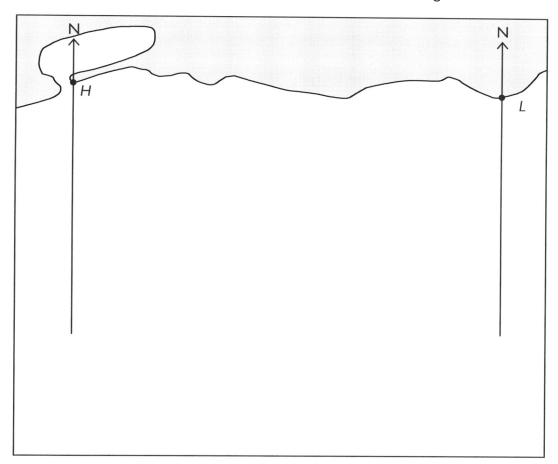

A rescue boat sets out from the harbour and sails straight to the windsurfer.

(i)   On the worksheet, show the route taken by the rescue boat. (2)

The position of the windsurfer from the lookout tower is on a bearing of 240°.

(ii) Mark the position of the windsurfer, *W*. (2)

The map above is drawn to a scale of 1 : 5000

(iii) How far is the windsurfer from the lookout tower? Give your answer
in metres. (3)

S3

■■□ 14. Clare walks 60 m on a bearing of 055° followed by 80 m on a bearing of 145°.

(i) Mark Clare's starting position (S) about halfway down the page, 4 cm from the left edge.

Using a scale of 1 : 1000, draw the first two stages of Clare's walk. (4)

(ii) What is the angle between the first two stages of Clare's walk? (1)

(iii) **Calculate** (do not measure) the distance Clare will have to walk in a straight line to return to her starting point. (3)

(iv) Which bearing will Clare take to walk back to S? (2)

15. (i) On a copy of the grid below, plot the points (3, 5), (6, 3) and (8, 6).

Join the points to form a triangle and label the triangle **A**. (2)

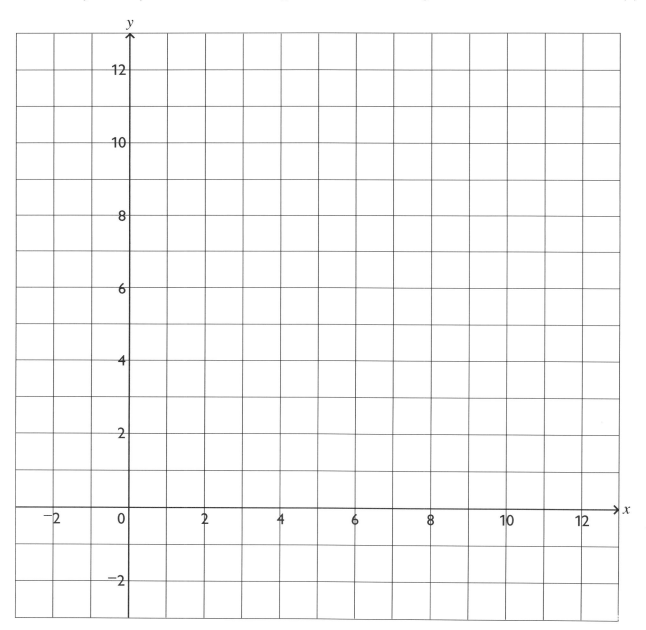

(ii) Draw the line $y = 2$ (1)

(iii) Reflect triangle **A** in the line $y = 2$ and label the image **B**.   (3)

(iv) Write down the co-ordinates of the vertices of triangle **B**.   (3)

16. (i) On a copy of the grid below, plot the point A (5, 3).   (1)

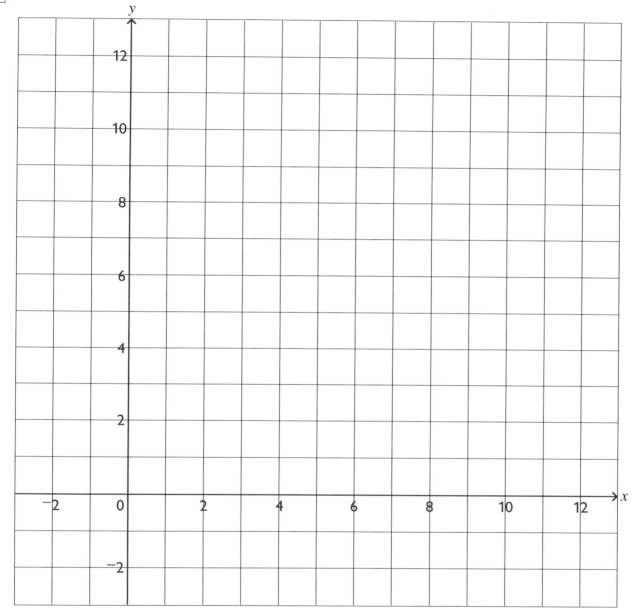

(ii) Reflect point A in the line $y = 5$ and label the image point B.   (1)

(iii) Reflect point B in the line $x = 2$ and label the image point C.   (1)

(iv) Draw:

    (a) triangle ABC (1)

    (b) the line $y = x$ (1)

(v) Reflect triangle ABC in the line $y = x$. Label the image A' B' C'.   (4)

17. (i) On a copy of the grid, plot the points (2, 1), (6, 4) and (6, 1). Join the points to form a triangle and label it **A**. (1)

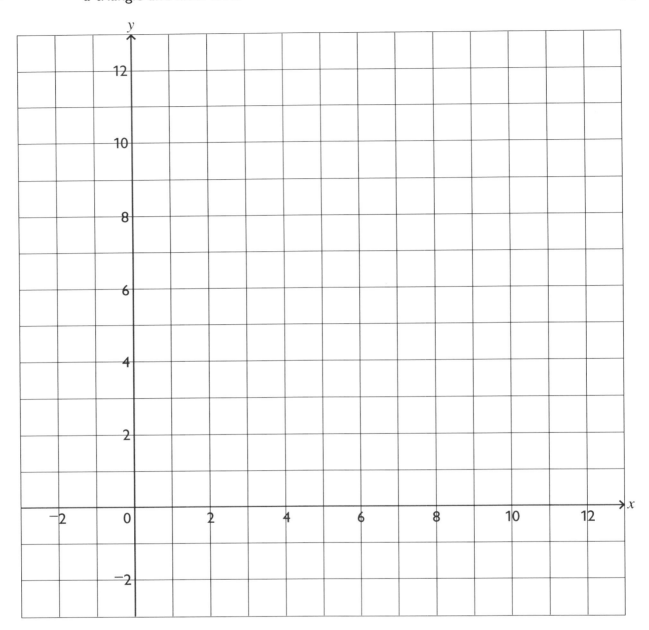

(ii) Draw the line whose equation is $y = 6$ (1)

(iii) Reflect triangle **A** in the line $y = 6$ and label the image triangle **B**. (2)

(iv) With the centre of rotation at the point (6, 1), rotate triangle **A** through 90° clockwise. Label the image triangle **C**. (2)

(v) On the grid, draw a fourth triangle so that the pattern made from the four triangles has one line of symmetry, and label the triangle **D**. (1)

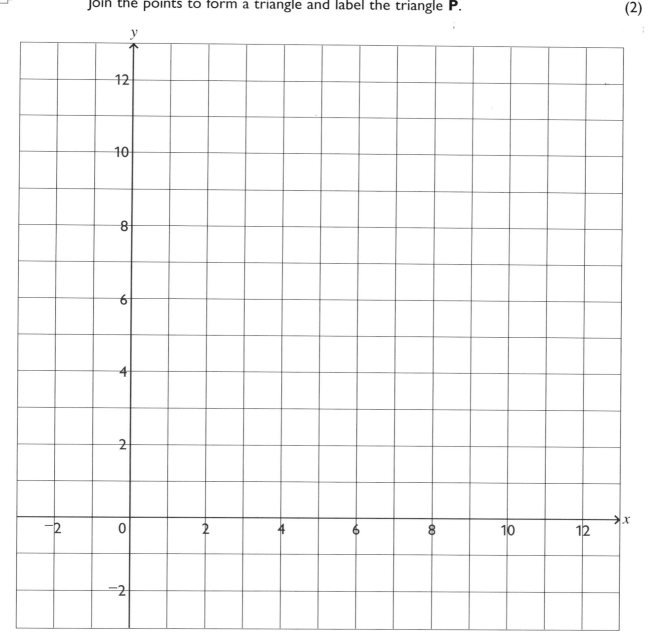

18. (i)   On a copy of the grid below, plot the points (1, 3), (4, 2) and (3, 4).
           Join the points to form a triangle and label the triangle **P**.   (2)

    (ii)   Reflect the triangle **P** in the line $x = 5$ and label the image triangle **Q**.   (2)

    (iii) Rotate the triangle **P** through 90° clockwise about the point (5, 5).
           Label the image triangle **R**.   (2)

    (iv)   Draw the mirror line which would map triangle **Q** onto triangle **R** by reflection. (2)

S3

■ ■ □ 19. Copy the diagram below.

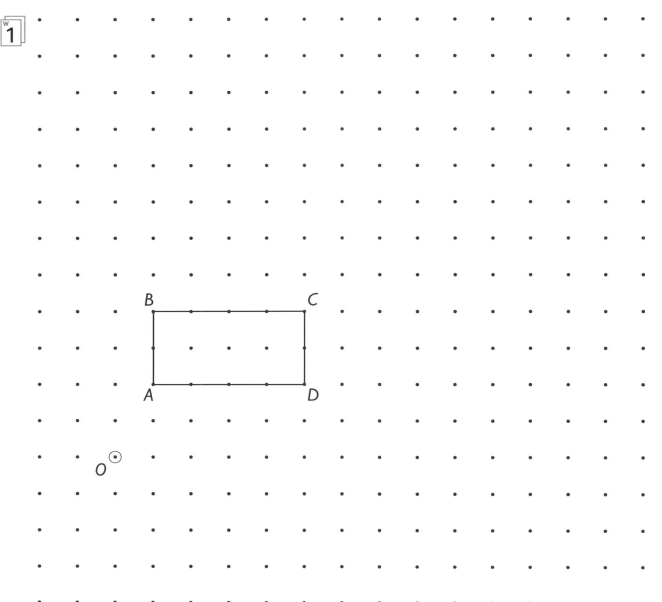

Draw the image of the shape *ABCD* when it has been enlarged by scale factor 2 with centre of enlargement *O*. (4)

■ ■ □ 20. Copy the diagram below.

B

C

A

(i) With centre *A*, enlarge triangle *ABC* by a scale factor 4 to give triangle *ADE*.
Label *D* and *E* clearly. (3)

Triangle *ABC* has an area of $2\frac{1}{2}$ cm^2.

(ii) Calculate the area of triangle *ADE*. (2)

S3

■ ■ ☐ 21. Copy the diagram below.

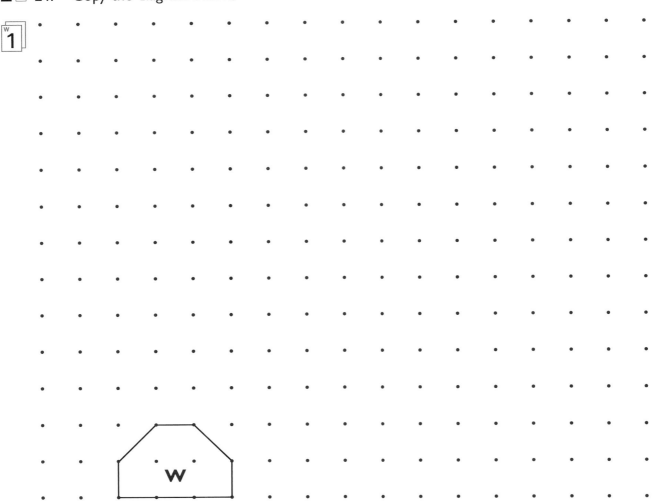

Shape **W** is drawn on a centimetre square dotted grid.

(i) With centre *O*, enlarge the shape **W**, using a scale factor of 3
Label the enlarged shape **X**. (3)

(ii) Find the area of the shape **W**. (2)

(iii) Hence, or otherwise, find the area of the enlarged shape **X**. (2)

■ ■ □ 22. Copy the diagram below.

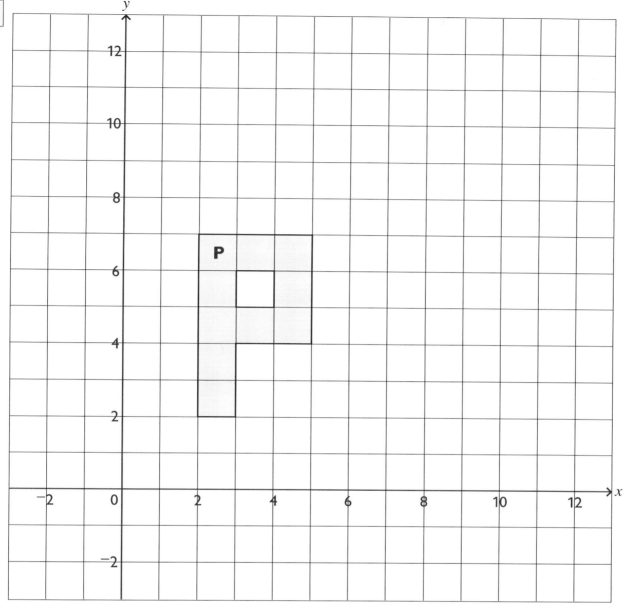

(i) With the point (⁻1, 3) as the centre of enlargement, enlarge shape **P** with a scale factor 2
Label the enlarged shape **Q**. (3)

(ii) What is the area of:

(a) shape **P** (2)

(b) shape **Q**? (2)

S3

■■□ 23. On the centimetre square grid below, *ABCDE* is a pentagon.

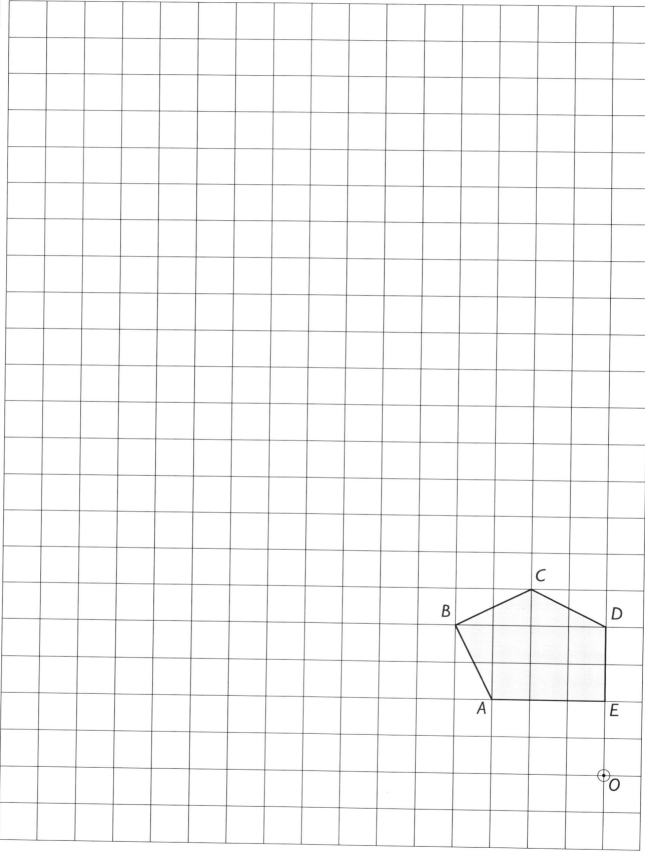

(i) What is the area of the pentagon *ABCDE*? (2)

(ii) If the pentagon *ABCDE* is enlarged with scale factor 4 what will be the area of the enlargement? (2)

(iii) On a copy of the diagram, with scale factor 4 and centre *O*, enlarge the pentagon *ABCDE*. (3)

S3

■■□ 24. On the grid below, shape **P** is made up of an isosceles triangle and two quadrants.

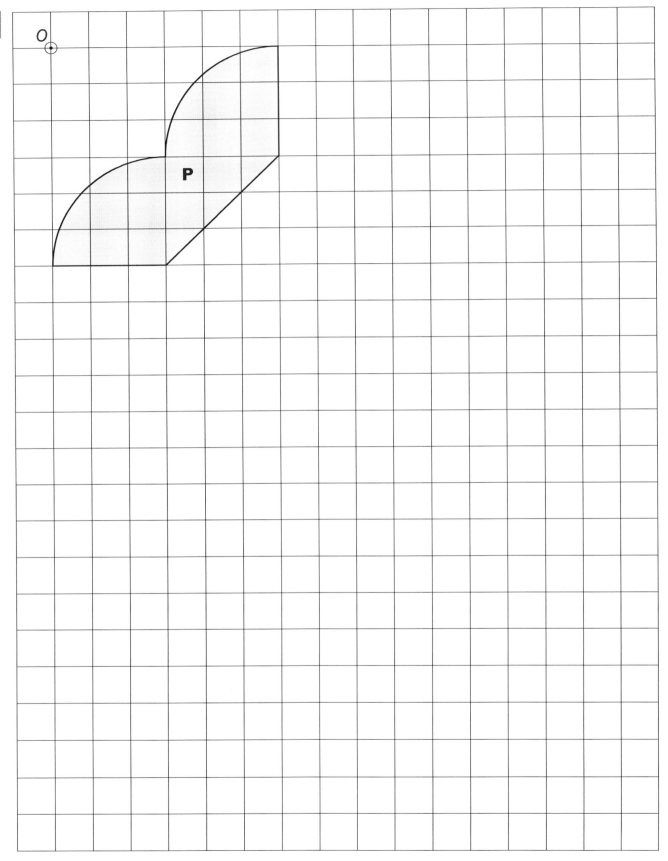

(i) With point *O* as the centre, enlarge shape **P** using a scale factor of 2
Label the image **Q**. (3)

(ii) Calculate the area of the shape **P**, taking the value of π to be 3 (3)

(iii) Hence, or otherwise, find the area of the enlarged shape **Q**. (2)

■■■ 25. (i) On a centimetre square co-ordinate grid:

(a) plot points *A* (3, 1), *B* (6, 1), *C* (8, 6) and *D* (5, 6) and join the points in order to form parallelogram *ABCD* (3)

(b) plot point *E* (3, 6) and draw triangle *DEA*. (1)

(ii) Calculate the area of:

(a) triangle *DEA* (1)

(b) parallelogram *ABCD*. (1)

(iii) Calculate, showing how you do this:

(a) the length of *AD* (2)

(b) the length of *AC*, the longest diagonal of the parallelogram *ABCD*. (2)

■■■ 26. (i) A rectangle measures 8 cm by 3.5 cm.

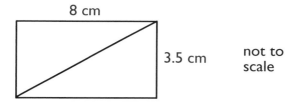

8 cm

3.5 cm

not to scale

Calculate the length of a diagonal of the rectangle. (2)

(ii) A box, in the shape of a cuboid, measures 8 cm by 3.5 cm by 4 cm.

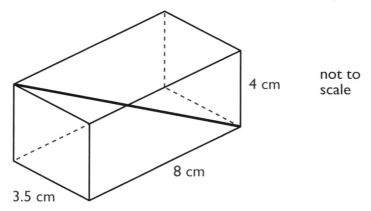

4 cm

not to scale

8 cm

3.5 cm

Calculate the length of the longest piece of rigid straight rod that could be fitted into the box. (4)

S3

■■■ 27. *ABCD* is a kite. The diagonals of the kite intersect at the point *P*.

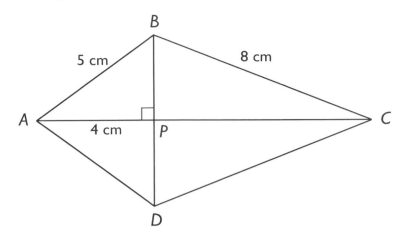

Angle *APB* is a right angle.

(i)   Calculate the length of the diagonal *BD*.   (2)

(ii) Calculate:

    (a)   the distance *PC*   (2)

    (b)   the length of the diagonal *AC*.   (1)

(iii) Calculate the area of the kite, giving your answer to 3 significant figures.   (2)

Extra – try this if you have studied trigonometry as an extension topic.

(iv) Calculate, giving your answers to the nearest degree:

    (a)   angle *BCP*   (3)

    (b)   angle *BCD*   (1)

    (c)   angle *ABC*.   (2)

Handling data

D1 Data handling

In this section the questions cover the following topics:

- Raw data and tallying
- Bar charts and frequency diagrams
- Range, mean, median and mode
- Pie charts
- Line graphs
- Conversion graphs
- Scatter diagrams

Many questions cover several topics.

Questions should, as far as possible, be answered without the use of a calculator.

1. In a class of 24 boys, each boy counted how many chips he had on his plate. The results were recorded as follows:

18	14	16	19	21	17	19	11	15	17	12	16
14	11	18	13	16	19	18	20	15	16	10	15

    (i)   What is the modal number of chips?   (1)

    (ii) Copy and complete the tally chart below.   (3)

Number of chips	Tally	Frequency
10–12		
13–15		
16–18		
19–21		
	Total	

    (iii) What is the probability that a boy, chosen at random, has on his plate:

    (a) 16 or more chips   (2)

    (b) fewer than 13 chips?   (2)

2. In a history test, the marks scored by a group of 18 students were:

6	9	6	5	7	7	10	4	7
5	8	7	10	6	6	9	8	6

D1

(i) Copy and complete the tally chart. (3)

Marks	Tally	Frequency
4	I	1
5		
6		
7		
8		
9		
10		
	Total	

(ii) What is the range of marks scored in the history test? (2)

(iii) For this set of marks, find:

(a) the mode (1)

(b) the median (2)

(c) the mean. (2)

3. Sean spun the pentagonal spinner below forty times and recorded his scores.

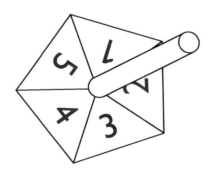

2	3	5	2	5	4	3	1	4	5
4	2	4	5	1	3	4	5	5	1
3	4	4	3	4	5	2	2	3	4
5	1	5	4	2	2	5	2	4	2

(i)   Copy and complete the tally chart.   (3)

Marks	Tally	Frequency
1		
2		
3		
4		
5		
	Total	

(ii) Copy and complete the frequency graph below.   (3)

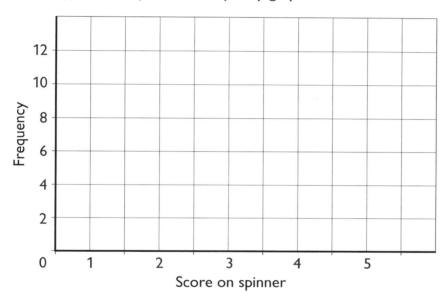

(iii) What is Sean's modal score?   (1)

(iv) What is his median score?   (2)

(v)   What is his mean score? Give your answer to 2 decimal places.   (3)

(vi) If Sean chooses one of his forty scores at random, what is the probability that it is:

(a)   an even number   (1)

(b)   a square number?   (1)

D1

4. Johnny kept a record of the goals scored in the term's soccer matches and drew the chart below.

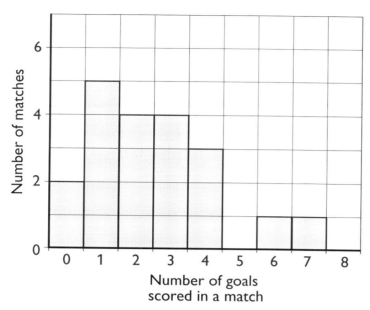

    (i)   How many matches did the team play?   (2)

    (ii) How many goals were scored altogether?   (2)

    (iii) What was the modal number of goals scored in a match?   (1)

    (iv) What was the median number of goals scored in a match?   (2)

    (v)   What was the mean number of goals scored in a match?   (2)

5. Two ice-hockey teams, Giants and Huskies, have played each other ten times. The numbers of goals scored by the two teams are shown in the table below.

Match	1	2	3	4	5	6	7	8	9	10
Giants	0	1	2	0	2	3	1	1	2	2
Huskies	3	1	1	3	0	1	3	0	2	1

    (i)   (a) What is the range of the number of goals scored per match by Giants?   (1)

          (b) What is the modal number of goals scored per match by Huskies?   (1)

          (c) What is the median number of goals scored per match by Giants?   (2)

    (ii) Which team:

          (a) won the larger number of matches   (2)

          (b) scored the larger number of goals?   (2)

6. Wendy has recorded the dress sizes of ten friends.

| 6 | 10 | 6 | 8 | 10 | 8 | 6 | 8 | 10 | 6 |

   (i)   Find the median dress size of Wendy's friends.   (2)

   (ii) What is the modal dress size?   (1)

■■□ 7. A group of 10 young athletes ran 200 metres and recorded their times, in seconds.

| 35.8 | 36.5 | 34.9 | 32.8 | 35.4 |
| 37.2 | 33.4 | 34.7 | 36.1 | 34.8 |

   (i)   For this set of data, calculate:

         (a) the range of times   (2)

         (b) the median time   (2)

         (c) the mean time.   (2)

   (ii) Giving your answers correct to 1 decimal place:

         (a) calculate, in metres/second, the average speed of the fastest athlete in
              the group   (2)

         (b) convert your answer to part (ii)(a) into kilometres/hour.   (2)

8. In Aviemore, the temperature at noon on each day between 1st December and 10th
   December is given in the table below.

Date	1st	2nd	3rd	4th	5th	6th	7th	8th	9th	10th
Temperature (°C)	0	−2	−1	0	0	1	3	−4	−3	0

   Calculate:

   (i)   the range of temperatures   (1)

   (ii) the modal temperature   (1)

   (iii) the median temperature   (2)

   (iv) the mean temperature.   (2)

■■□ 9. A market stall sells bags of mixed vegetables. Each bag contains 40 vegetables. There are
   10 potatoes, 8 carrots, 18 sprouts and the rest are parsnips.

   (i)   How many parsnips are there?   (1)

   (ii) Draw a pie chart to show the different kinds of vegetables in a bag. Clearly mark
         each sector with both the angle and the name of the vegetable.   (5)

   Jennifer bought one bag and cooked half of the total number of vegetables. She cooked all
   the parsnips, a third of the sprouts, half of the carrots and some potatoes.

   (iii) What fraction of the potatoes did Jennifer cook?   (3)

D1

117

10. Rowena recorded the colours of coats worn by people passing the window. She started to construct the pie chart shown below.

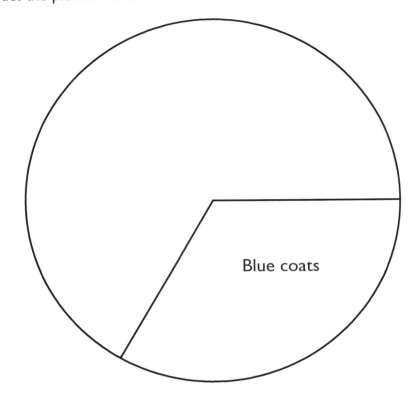

Blue coats

(i) Measure the angle of the sector representing people wearing blue coats. (1)

Twelve people were wearing blue coats.

(ii) What size of angle represents one person? (1)

(iii) Copy and complete the table below. (3)

Colour of coat	Number of people	Size of angle on pie chart
Blue	12	
Red		
Green	5	
Black	8	
Yellow		70°
Total		360°

(iv) How many people were wearing red coats? (2)

(v) Copy and complete Rowena's pie chart. (4)

11. A pie chart is to be drawn to represent the favourite chocolate bars of the twenty-four members of a class.

   (i)   What angle will represent each student?   (2)

   Nine of the students said that their favourite chocolate bar was *Jupiter*.

   (ii) What is the angle of the sector which will represent these students?   (2)

   Thrix is the favourite chocolate bar of six of the children.

   (iii) What fraction of the children is this?   (2)

12. Sandy carried out a survey of the favourite pop group of each member of his class. He started to construct a pie chart, but lost some data so he hasn't completed it.

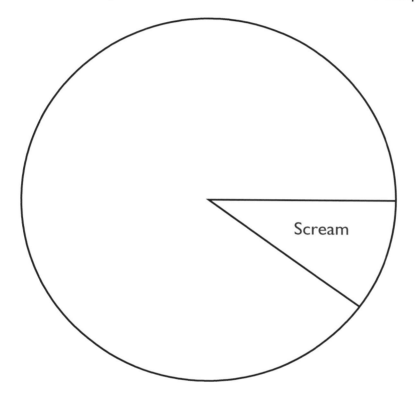

   Sandy knows that two people chose *Scream*.

   The pie chart is accurately constructed so far.

   (i)   How many members are there in Sandy's class?   (1)

   Sandy can remember that exactly three times as many chose *Gruntalot* as chose *Scream*.

D1

119

(ii) Copy and complete Sandy's data table. (5)

Pop group	Number of children	Size of angle on pie chart
Scream	2	36°
Grubby	3	
Sloppydress		
Gruntalot		
Total		360°

(iii) What is the probability that a student, picked at random from the survey:

    (a) chose *Grubby* (2)

    (b) did not choose *Sloppydress*? (2)

13. A farm of 240 hectares grows three main crops:

oil seed rape	*150 hectares*
barley	*60 hectares*
wheat	*30 hectares*

This information is to be illustrated by a pie chart.

(i) How many degrees will represent one hectare? (1)

(ii) Copy and complete the table below, showing the angles of the pie chart sectors. (3)

Crop	Size of angle on pie chart
Oil seed rape	
Barley	
Wheat	

■■□ (iii) Draw a pie chart and label each sector with the name of the crop. (3)

14. Some children were asked to choose an ice-cream. The choices were as shown below.

ICE CREAMS 60p each
Vanilla
Strawberry
Mint
Chocolate

Two fifths of the children chose either vanilla or strawberry and a third of this group chose vanilla. The information is to be recorded as a pie chart.

(i) What is the angle of the sector representing those who chose:

    (a) vanilla   (2)

    (b) strawberry?   (1)

9 children chose mint and 18 more children chose chocolate than chose mint.

(ii) (a) How many children chose mint or chocolate?   (1)

    (b) What angle represents the children who chose mint or chocolate?   (2)

(iii) How many degrees represent each child?   (2)

(iv) Copy and complete the table below.   (2)

Flavour	Number of children	Size of angle on pie chart
Vanilla		
Strawberry		
Mint		
Chocolate		
Total		

■■□ 15. (i) *Smith's Garden Centre* sells boxes of mixed bulbs. Each box of bulbs contains a gross (144) of which a third are daffodils and $\frac{1}{8}$ are tulips.

In addition, there are 2 dozen crocuses and the rest are snowdrops.
Draw a fully labelled pie chart to show this information.
Mark each sector clearly with both angle and name of bulb.   (5)

D1

(ii) *Flora's Garden Centre* also sells boxes containing a gross of mixed bulbs.

The pie chart below shows the proportion of bulbs in their mixture.

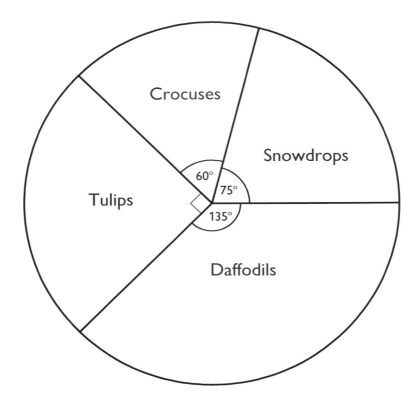

(a) What percentage of the bulbs in this box are daffodils? (2)

(b) How many snowdrops are in this box? (2)

16. Below is a graph which could be used for converting British pounds (£) into US dollars ($) one day in December 2010

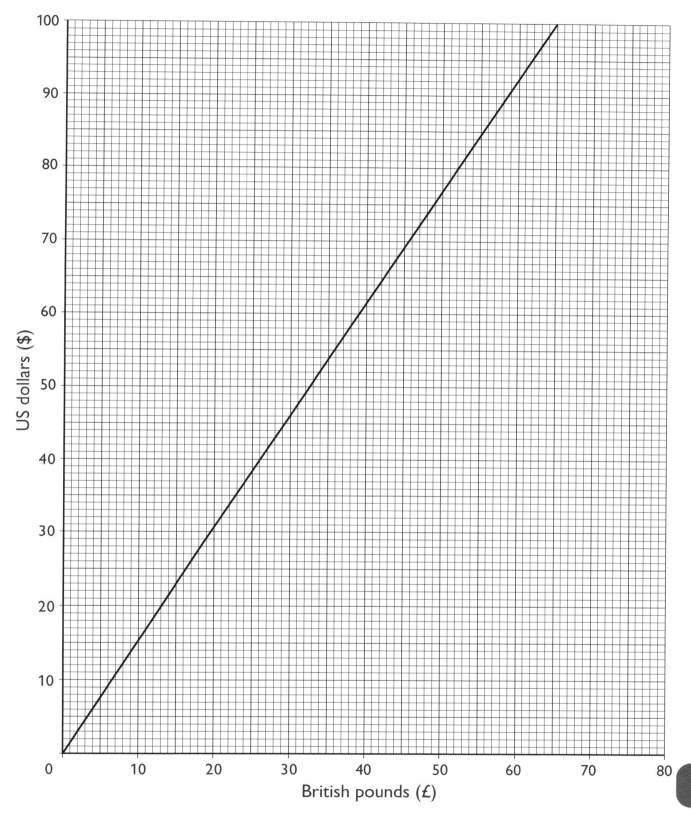

(i) On your worksheet, marking clearly where you take your readings, find:

(a) how many dollars were equivalent to £45 (2)

(b) how many pounds were equivalent to $80 (2)

(ii) On a flight from New York to London, a duty free bottle of perfume was priced at $55
In the airport duty free shop, the same item was priced at £37
Which price was the better value? Mark the graph clearly to support your answer. (2)

■■□ 17. In this question use the conversion:

1 kilogram (kg) is the equivalent of 2.2 pounds (lb)

(i) On a copy of the grid below, draw a graph to convert kilograms into pounds. (2)

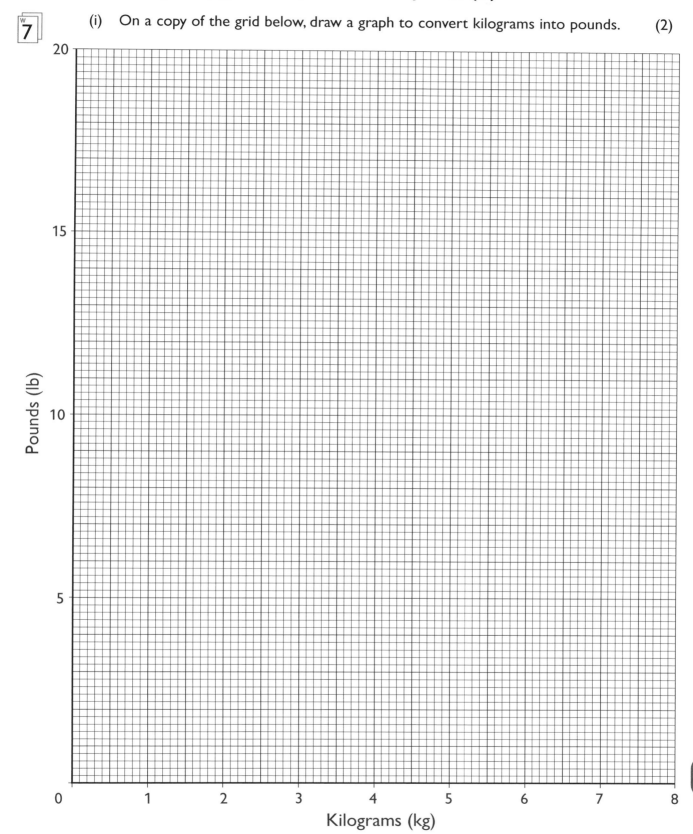

D1

(ii) Use your graph, showing clearly where you take your readings, to answer the following questions.

(a) A sack of potatoes has a mass of 18 kg. What is the equivalent mass in pounds? Give your answer to the nearest pound. (2)

(b) Fiona needs $1\frac{1}{2}$ pounds of flour to make a cake.
How many grams of flour does Fiona need? (2)

■■□ 18. Stephen went to France on a day trip.
1 pound (GBP) was equivalent to 1.3 euros (EUR).
At the start of the trip, Stephen changed 200 pounds into euros.

(i) How many euros did he receive? (1)

Stephen drew a conversion graph

7

(ii) On a copy of this grid, complete the scales on the axes and draw a graph to show the conversion of pounds to euros. (4)

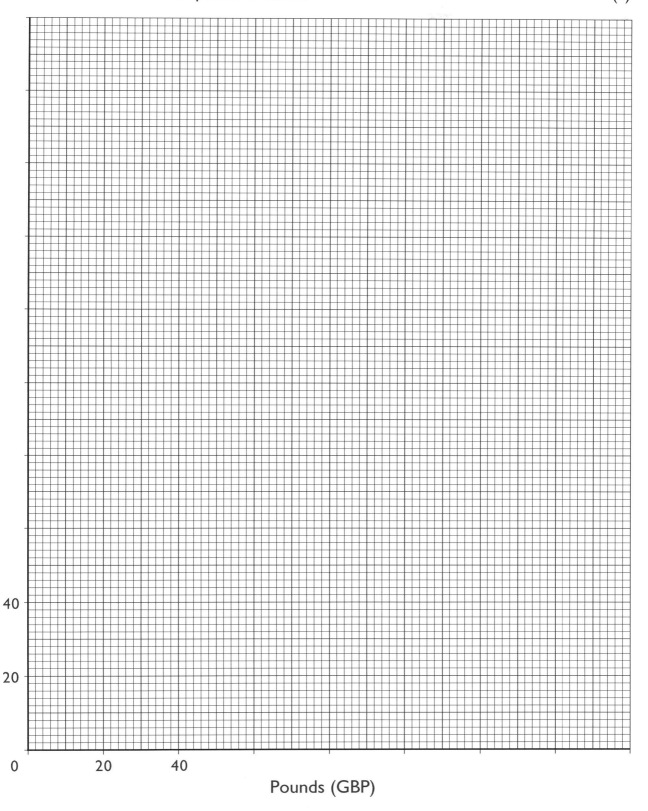

Euros (EUR)

40

20

0   20   40

Pounds (GBP)

D1

Stephen bought a jacket priced at **98** euros.

(iii) Showing clearly where you take your reading, use your graph to find the equivalent price in pounds, to the nearest pound. (2)

At the end of his trip, Stephen had **37** euros left.

(iv) How many pounds, to the nearest pound, would he receive for this? (2)

■■□ 19. In this question use the conversion rate:

1 hectare (ha) is equivalent to 2.47 acres

(i) How many acres are equivalent to 80 hectares? Give your answer to the nearest acre.

(2)

7

(ii) On a copy of the grid below, draw a graph for converting areas up to 80 hectares to acres.

(3)

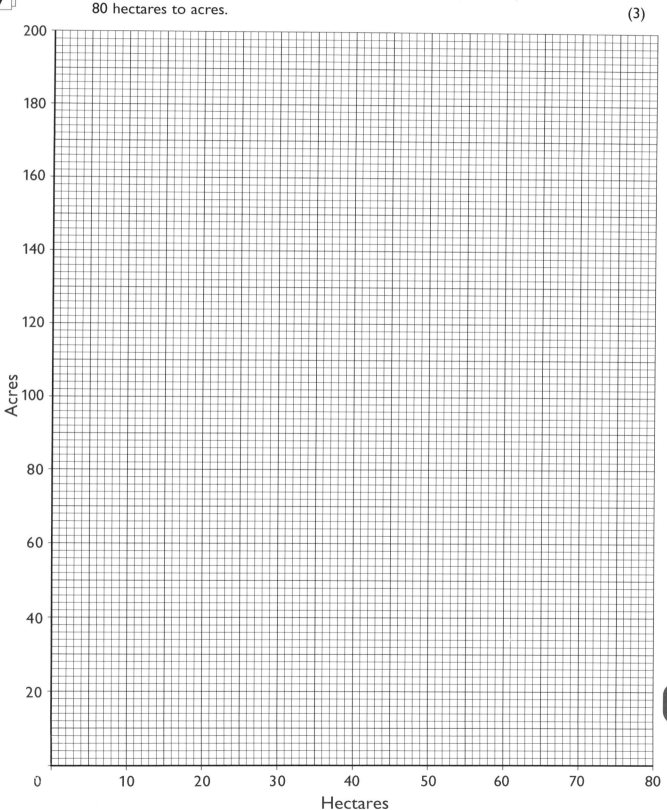

D1

(iii) Use your graph to answer the following questions, showing clearly where you take your readings.

    (a) A park has an area of 23 hectares. How many acres is this? (2)

    (b) A forest covers 180 acres. How many hectares is this? (2)

20. In this question use the conversion:

1 euro (EUR) is equivalent to 0.8 pounds (GBP)

(i) What is the value, in pounds, of 40 euros? (1)

(ii) Copy the grid below, complete the scales and draw a graph to show the conversion of euros to pounds up to 40 euros. (2)

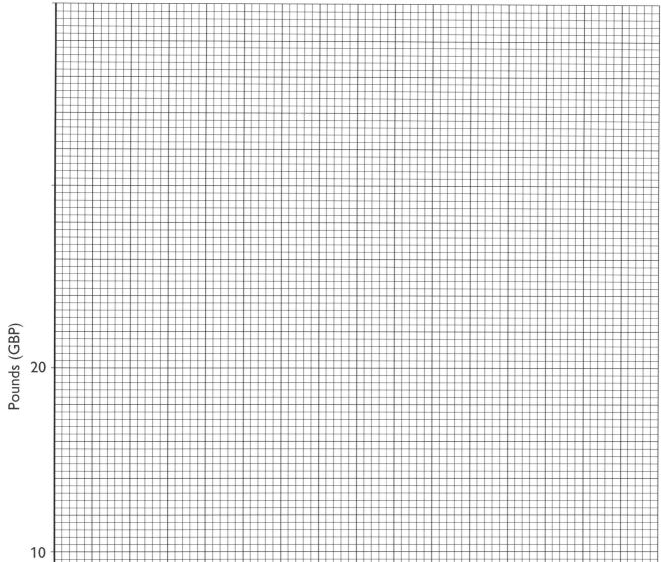

Pounds (GBP)

Euros (EUR)

(iii) Showing clearly where you take your readings, use your graph to find:

    (a) how many pounds Virginie will receive in exchange for 30 euros   (2)

    (b) how many euros Eddie will receive for 30 pounds.   (2)

21.   In a scientific study, Katie measured the length and width of 10 leaves collected from beneath a tree. The results are given in the table below.

Width (mm)	34	40	29	35	43	32	38	41	36	31
Length (mm)	65	84	60	96	84	61	73	79	74	62

(i) On a copy of the grid below, complete the scales on the axes and represent the data as a scatter diagram. (5)

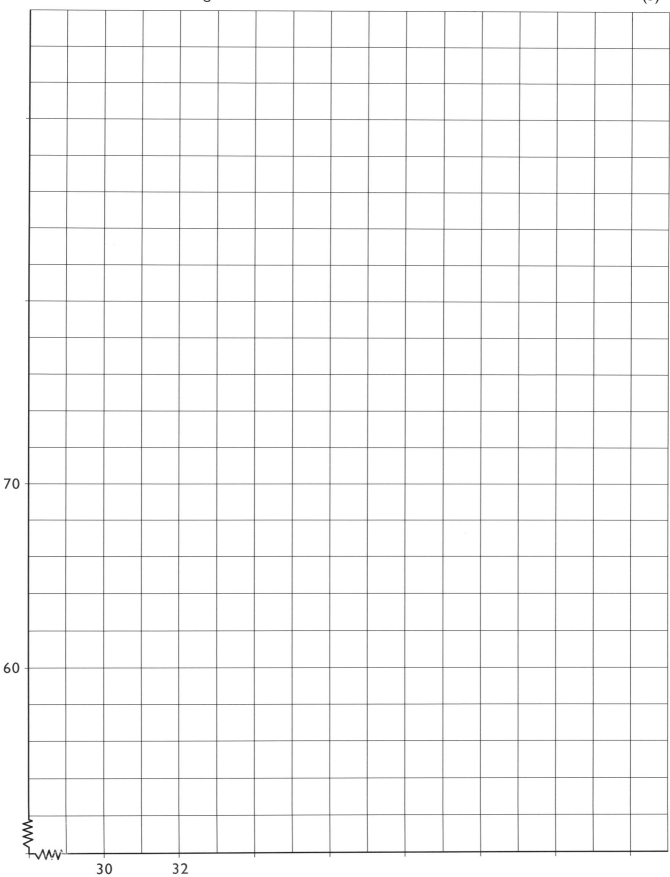

Length (mm)

70

60

30   32

Width (mm)

133

D1

Katie thinks that one of the leaves might be from a different tree.

(ii) Circle the point on the grid which represents the leaf which might have come from a different tree. (1)

(iii) Ignoring the point circled in part (ii), draw the line of best fit. (1)

(iv) What sort of correlation do these results show? (1)

(v) Use your line of best fit to find the approximate ratio of length to width of the leaves. Show clearly where you take any readings. (2)

22. Simon has taken some measurements of the hands of adults in his family.

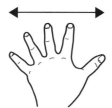 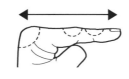

He has measured:

● handspan (at full stretch)

● index finger length (from start of knuckle to finger tip).

The table below shows the data.

Handspan (cm)	24	22	25	20	21	19	23	18
Index finger length (cm)	11	10	11.5	9.5	10	9	12	8.5

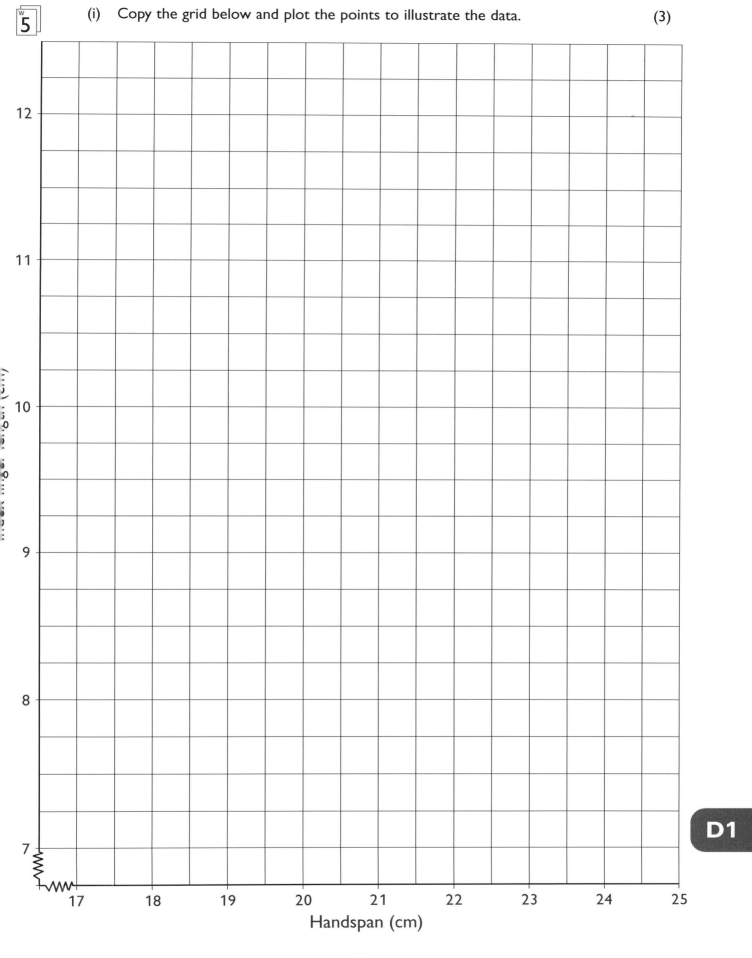

5   (i)   Copy the grid below and plot the points to illustrate the data.   (3)

Handspan (cm)

D1

■■□   (ii) Draw the line of best fit.   (1)

Uncle Albert, who did not take part in Simon's study, has a handspan of 23 cm.

(iii) Estimate the index finger length of Uncle Albert, showing how you obtained
your answer.   (2)

23. Seventeen young athletes took part in the 200 metres and the high jump. The scatter graph below records the results of the first twelve competitors.

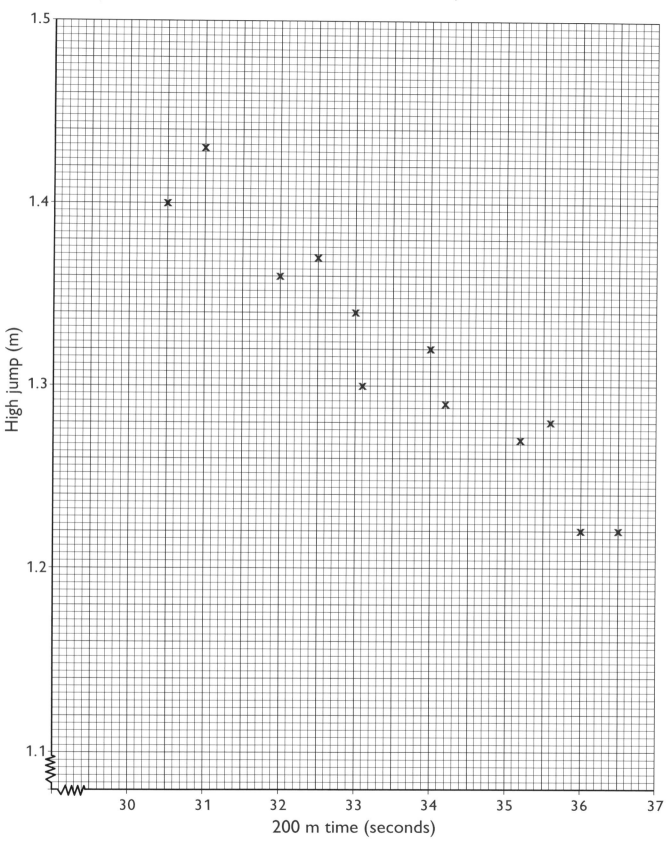

D1

The table below records the results for the last five competitors.

Competitor	200 m time (seconds)	High jump (m)
Paula (P)	36.6	1.20
Quentin (Q)	35.2	1.25
Robin (R)	31.3	1.40
Sian (S)	32.5	1.34
Tim (T)	33.7	1.36

(i) On your worksheet, plot and label these results. (2)

(ii) Which type of correlation does your scatter graph suggest? (1)

(iii) Suggest a reason for this correlation. (1)

(iv) Draw the line of best fit on the scatter graph. (1)

Ursula was away for the 200 m trials but she recorded a high jump of 1.44 m.

(v) Use your line of best fit to estimate the time which Ursula might have recorded in the 200 m event, if she is typical of the group. (2)

Victor pulled a muscle in the high jump and had to retire, but he had recorded a time of 34.5 seconds in the 200 metres.

(vi) Suggest the height Victor might have achieved if he had not been injured. (2)

D2 Probability

In this section the questions cover the following topics:

● Outcomes of events

● Probability

Questions should, as far as possible, be answered without the use of a calculator.

1. Julian tosses a fair coin and Ellie spins a pentagonal spinner at the same time.

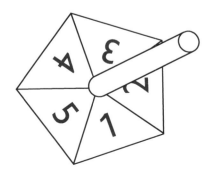

Julian records H for 'head' and T for 'tail' and Ellie records the score.

(i) Copy and complete this table of all the possible outcomes. (2)

H	and	1
H	and	
	and	
	and	
	and	

T	and	
	and	
	and	
	and	
	and	

(ii) What is the probability that:

    (a) Julian gets a head and Ellie gets an odd number (1)

    (b) Julian gets a tail and Ellie gets a square number? (1)

2. (a) Brian and Henry are playing a game. Each boy has written the letters of his name on separate cards and placed the cards in his pocket.

Each boy takes a card at random from his pocket. Brian takes A and Henry takes E. They record the result in a table.

	H	E	N	R	Y
B					
R					
I					
A		AE			
N					

    (i) Copy and complete the table above to show all the possible combinations. (3)

    (ii) What is the probability that the two cards taken will have the same letter? (2)

    (iii) What is the probability that the two cards taken will both have a consonant? (2)

(b) The probability that a train does **not** arrive late in Waffle is $\frac{5}{7}$
A total of 56 trains arrive in Waffle each week.
How many of these would you expect to be late? (2)

D2

3. Nancy has a square spinner and a pentagonal spinner.

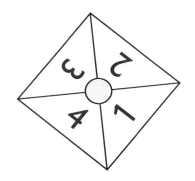 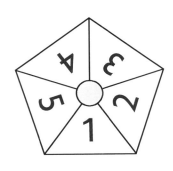

She spins the spinners and multiplies the two scores.

(i) Copy and complete the table of possible outcomes. (3)

	score on pentagonal spinner				
×	1	2	3	4	5
1					
2					
3		6			
4				16	

score on square spinner

(ii) Simplifying your answers as much as possible, find the probability that the result is:

(a) 6 (2)

(b) an odd number (2)

(c) a square number (1)

(d) ten or larger. (2)

Nancy asks Barry to choose, at random, a number between 1 and 20 inclusive.

(iii) What is the probability that Barry chooses a number which is **not** in the table? (2)

4. A box contains some coloured sweets.
The pictogram below shows the numbers of coloured sweets in a box.
One symbol represents 1 sweet.

Colour

Blue ○○○○○

Red ○○○○

Green ○○○○○○○

Yellow ○○

Pink ○○○○○

140

One sweet is taken at random from the box.

(i) What is the probability of taking a pink sweet? Give your answer as a fraction in its lowest terms. (2)

(ii) What is the probability of **not** taking a blue sweet? (2)

5. In *Lotto*, a machine puts out, at random, any one of the first 49 counting numbers (1 to 49 inclusive) as the first number.

(i) What is the probability that the first number will be:

(a) 20 (1)

(b) even (2)

(c) prime? (3)

The first number chosen is 5 and the machine now puts out a second number.

(ii) What is the probability that the second number will be

(a) 20 (1)

(b) odd? (2)

6. Jamie rolls an ordinary, fair die.

(i) What is the probability that the die shows:
(a) 3 (1)
(b) a square number (2)
(c) a prime number? (2)

Jamie rolls the die 120 times and records the scores.

(ii) How many times might he expect to roll:
(a) 6 (1)
(b) a number less than 3? (2)

When he has finished, Jamie adds the 120 scores.

(iii) Estimate the total score, showing clearly how you do this. (2)

7. In Sacha's pocket are four 1p coins, six 5p coins and two 20p coins. Sacha pulls out a coin at random.

    (i)   What is the probability that the coin is:

        (a) a 1p   (2)

        (b) either a 5p or a 20p?   (2)

Sacha puts the coin back in his pocket. He now pulls out **two** coins.

    (ii) What is the probability that the first coin is a 5p?   (1)

The first coin is a 5p and Sacha puts this coin on the table. He does **not** put it back in his pocket.

    (iii) What is the probability that the second coin is a 5p?   (2)

8. In Mary's sewing kit there are w white buttons and g green buttons. There are more white buttons than green buttons.

    (i)   Giving your answers in terms of w and g, write down:

        (a) the number of buttons in the kit   (1)

        (b) how many more white buttons there are than green buttons.   (2)

Mary picks a button at random.

    (ii) What is the probability that she picks:

        (a) a white button   (1)

        (b) a green button?   (1)

The button is green but Mary drops it and can't find it. She picks another button at random.

    (iii) What is the probability that this button is also green?   (2)

9. The letters of the word **Pythagoras** are written on cards as shown.

P	Y	T	H	A	G	O	R	A	S

The cards are shuffled and then turned over. Lorna takes one card at random.

    (i)   What is the probability that Lorna takes:

        (a) G   (1)

        (b) A   (1)

        (c) U?   (1)

Lorna takes letter A and does **not** replace the card. She takes another card at random.

(ii) What is the probability that this time Lorna takes:

    (a) G   (1)

    (b) A   (1)

    (c) a vowel?   (2)

Lorna replaces both cards. She takes a card.

(iii) What is the probability that this letter has:

    (a) line symmetry **only**   (2)

    (b) rotational symmetry **only**   (1)

    (c) both line and rotational symmetry   (2)

    (d) no symmetry at all.   (1)

10. There are twelve children at a party.

If a child is chosen at random:

- the probability that it will be a girl is $\frac{2}{3}$

- the probability that he/she likes playing 'hide and seek' is $\frac{3}{4}$

Only one of the boys does not like playing 'hide and seek'.

(i) Represent this information as:

    (a) a Carroll diagram   (2)

    (b) a Venn diagram.   (2)

The names of the children are written on pieces of paper and put in a hat. One name is chosen at random:

(ii) What is the probability that the child will be:

    (a) a boy who enjoys playing 'hide and seek'   (2)

    (b) a girl who does not enjoy playing 'hide and seek'?   (2)

11. Jemima, Joanna and Jasmine have been comparing the letters in their names.
The letters used in Jemima's name are, in alphabetical order, A, E, I, J, M.
Note that M is listed only once although there are two Ms in Jemima's name.

(i) List, in alphabetical order:

    (a) the letters used in the name JOANNA   (1)

    (b) the letters used in the name JASMINE   (1)

    (c) the alphabet letters which are not used in any of their names.   (2)

D2

The girls have started to write the 26 letters of the alphabet in a Venn diagram.

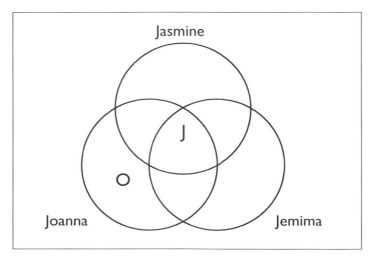

(ii) Copy and complete the Venn diagram, **remembering that each alphabet letter goes in just once**. (4)

A letter of the alphabet is chosen at random.

(iii) What is the probability that it will:

(a) not be in any of the girls' names (2)

(b) be in at least two of the girls' names? (2)

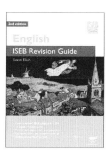
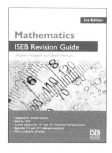

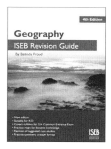

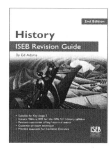
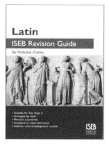

   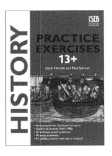 
 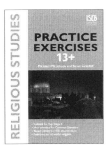   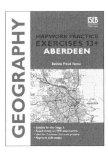

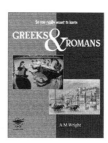